1985

CULTIVATING AGRICULTURAL LITERACY:

CHALLENGE FOR THE LIBERAL ARTS

CULTIVATING AGRICULTURAL LITERACY:

CHALLENGE FOR THE LIBERAL ARTS

Gordon K. Douglass
Editor

A review and analysis of 11 pacesetting experiments funded by the W. K. Kellogg Foundation to generate greater awareness among liberal arts students and faculty about the role and importance of the agriculture enterprise to the nation.

Published by the W. K. Kellogg Foundation
Battle Creek, Michigan

January 1985

Opinions and conclusions expressed in this publication are those of the authors and do not necessarily represent those of the W. K. Kellogg Foundation.

CONTENTS

APPENDICES

FOREWORD

Few issues are of greater importance to the world than adequate food supplies, proper food use, and knowledge about the components of the agricultural industry. Yet today most people, including those in key positions of public decision-making, do not understand the complexities of America's food system; nor do they fully comprehend its relationship to human nutrition or its impact on international trade and relations.

As Stephen Bailey, former vice president for the American Council on Education, said: "This nation is in woefully short supply of people equipped to look at *problems* as a whole, at *life* as a whole. Without a sense of the whole, we have no way of evaluating the part . . . ."

People's inability to look at problems in their entirety, instead of seeing only isolated fragments, is especially severe in regard to agriculture issues. The production of food — agriculture — is the basic human enterprise, yet each decade fewer people have a full appreciation for this reality. That is not surprising in light of several sobering facts.

Fewer and fewer people in the United States have direct involvement in farming or production of crops and livestock. The population of the United States exceeds 235 million; only 3 percent of that number live on farms. Ninety percent of the population has been nonfarm for over 30 years. Four-fifths of the working population is employed in jobs that have no connection with agricultural processing and distribution enterprises or businesses that supply farming equipment or materials. Of the 13 million college students in the nation, only 152,500 are majoring in agricultural disciplines. Few nonagricultural students elect to take *any* agricultural courses, though they may eventually hold leadership positions which require them to make decisions on matters affecting agriculture and human nutrition. Decisions on zoning, banking, foreign trade, location of highways, and property taxation are but just a few examples of actions that affect the agricultural enterprise.

Recognizing the gravity of this situation, the W. K. Kellogg Foundation has been helping institutions find new ways to prepare individuals who can look at agricultural issues in the context of society's broad goals. In 1976 the Foundation began to encourage the incorporation of education on food/agriculture/natural resources in liberal arts undergraduate curricula. The goal, obviously, was to promote greater awareness and understanding among students and faculty about the role and importance of agriculture to the nation and to the world.

To date, 16 liberal arts colleges and 12 land-grant universities have been assisted. All are working to establish agriculture-in-the-liberal arts or agriculture-in-the-humanities programs.

Cultivating Agricultural Literacy details the pacesetting experiments of the first 11 institutions funded by the Foundation. It is based on presentations made by these colleges and universities at a Kellogg Foundation-supported dissemination conference held at the University of Florida, Gainesville, in January 1984. More than 430 representatives from 63 land-grant universities and 57 private liberal arts colleges attended the three-day event. Project results were discussed, including an examination of approaches used by the 11 institutions.

The chapters that follow explain in detail how these various institutions, all different in size and structure, brought agricultural knowledge to liberal learning. Topics described include program planning, curricular development, and program outcomes.

Because each experiment had its instructive successes and its instructive failures, descriptions of both are found in this book. They are intended to guide other colleges and universities that want to help liberal arts students — tomorrow's national and local decision makers — to understand agriculture and its relationship to pressing world issues.

Cultivating Agricultural Literacy is a resource tool. It is offered to all administrators, faculty members, students, and policymakers who are dedicated to finding the best way to help Americans view agricultural issues as a whole. It is recommended for all persons who are concerned with the wise management and use of our natural resources, and with the assurance of an adequate supply of nutritious food for future generations.

Russell G. Mawby
Chairman of the Board and
Chief Executive Officer
W. K. Kellogg Foundation

Chapter 1

The Need for Agricultural Awareness

Gordon K. Douglass

Ten liberal arts colleges, scattered across the nation, have served during the last few years as laboratories for a unique educational experiment designed to determine, if it is possible — or desirable — to infuse a liberal arts curriculum with information about agriculture. Some of these colleges still are in the initial stages of the experiment, others have fully tested ways to offer liberal arts students coursework on agriculture and food production topics. In either case, sufficient knowledge has been accumulated to summarize what has been learned about the advantages and hazards of implementing such "Agriculture-in-the-Liberal Arts" programs.

The colleges involved in the experiment include: Adrian College, Adrian, Michigan; Briar Cliff College, Sioux City, Iowa; Coe College, Cedar Rapids, Iowa; Cornell College, Mt. Vernon, Iowa; Earlham College, Richmond, Indiana; Grinnell College, Iowa; Luther College, Decorah, Iowa; Pomona College, Claremont, California; Williams College, Williamstown, Massachusetts; and Wilmington College, Ohio. Four of these colleges — Coe, Cornell, Grinnell, and Luther — are yoked in a cooperative program which centralizes some training of faculty. All the institutions have been encouraged in their work through grants from the W. K. Kellogg Foundation of Battle Creek, Michigan.

The Kellogg Foundation also has given its support to the University of Florida, Gainesville, to develop a "Humanities and Agriculture" program with similar purposes. The setting of the University of Florida program is dramatically different, however. One of America's leading land-grant institutions, it is composed of 18 professional schools and colleges, including a College of Liberal Arts and Sciences where its agriculture-in-the-liberal arts

Gordon K. Douglass is James Irvine Professor of economics and chairman of the steering committee for the Food, Land & Power program at Pomona College, Claremont, CA.

program is located. But the presence of a school of agriculture (the Institute of Food and Agricultural Sciences) on campus has given the organizers of the Humanities of Agriculture program direct access to people fully knowledgeable about agricultural science — a luxury unavailable to most liberal arts colleges. It also has provided a challenging opportunity to help agricultural students and faculty to broaden their ways of thinking about the field.

The University of Florida *is* different from the liberal arts colleges participating in the experiment, as will become apparent in the reading of Chapter 9; but that is not the main point to be made in this introduction. Rather, the point is that each participating institution brought to the experiment a unique set of attributes and a distinctive sense of mission. No doubt all experimental institutions subscribe to the notion of liberal learning — of cultivating rigorous thought and fostering interest among students in humanity and its universe. But their faculties, student bodies, settings, institutional histories, affiliations, calendars, governance structures, and resource bases are sufficiently different that their responses to the challenges of liberal learning are varied. In short, the experiences described in Chapters 2 through 9 are products of the environments in which they were nurtured. Thus every college and university interested in exploring agricultural approaches to liberal learning will find something useful to their particular needs.

Purpose*

Before describing the programs that relate agriculture to the liberal arts, it is necessary to ask how practitioners of agriculture in the liberal arts justify their work. After all, the traditions of higher education have succeeded in keeping the "useful arts" and the "liberal arts" separate in the curriculum up to now. Why then should they be fitted together in some new design?

The answers can be drawn from history and from new realizations of the physical, social, and political limits to the world's ability to feed itself.

---

* This section draws heavily on an address by the author at a conference on "Food/ Agriculture in the Liberal Arts," University of Florida, Gainesville, January 3-7, 1984.

The debate over whether education should be "liberal" or "useful" certainly isn't new. Aristotle began it by asking: "Should the useful in life, or should virtue, or should the higher knowledge be the aim of our training?" "All three opinions have been entertained," he noted, but "no one knows on what principle we should proceed."[1] There followed through the centuries an uneasy division of labor, first between religious training for priests and vocational training for others; then, after establishment of medieval universities, between classical education for freemen destined for roles of responsibility and vocational training for others. When, in the Nineteenth Century, Oxford University's classical education was criticized "for its remoteness from practical life,"[2] Cardinal Newman came to its defense by rejecting as inappropriate to the university "particular and narrow ends," and argued instead that a "liberal" education was "truly and fully useful, though it not be a professional education."[3]

The debate was joined in America at the time populism inspired the land-grant movement. Some, like Thorstein Veblen, continued to object to the inclusion of business, engineering, farming, and other practical subjects in the curriculum of higher learning. Others, probably a majority, held views similar to Alfred Whitehead who believed "the main justification for a university is that it preserves the connection between knowledge and the zest for life." "It is a libel on human nature," he added, "to conceive that zest for life is the product of pedestrian purposes directed toward the narrow routine of material comforts."[4] Even so, there was an uneasy feeling that mixing the liberal and useful arts carried significant intellectual hazards. Whitehead himself warned, for example, that "necessary technical excellence can only be acquired by a teaching which is apt to damage those energies of mind which should direct the technical skill."[5]

Higher education grew rapidly and changed profoundly after World War II. The field of formal education became professionalized. As a result disciplinary departments were strengthened. Research was elevated above teaching in many institutions, thereby limiting the time and opportunity available to younger faculty members to explore topics in breadth outside of their own fields. Faculty specialists earned the right to teach only their specialties. And, large professional schools blossomed at most universities (ironically, these sometimes became the cash cows which made possible continuance of liberal studies). For all these reasons — and more — the power to decide what to teach and how to teach it shifted accordingly. This shift left essentially no one in charge of maintaining a coherent and liberating curriculum as an anchor for student understanding. Even many liberal arts colleges responded to the pressures of the times by professionalizing their curriculums and adapting to the demands of vocationalism.[6]

Within the last few years, a modest revival of interest in the liberal arts has taken place among educational leaders. Convinced that "the disciplines are an inadequate basis for the organization of liberal learning," they are seeking more sophisticated and comprehensive models to develop in students a "sense of calling, in which life and career are integrated."[7]

By reciting this brief history of the tension between the liberal arts and the useful arts, practitioners of agriculture-in-the-liberal arts make clear both their concern about the weakened state of the liberal arts and their optimism about the potential of developing models for a coherent liberal arts curriculum. They do not agree with the view represented by the narrator of Robert Persig's *Zen and the Art of Motorcycle Maintenance.* Persig maintains that the liberal arts and the useful arts " . . .are *two* realities, one of immediate artistic appearance and one of underlying scientific explanation, and they don't really have much of anything to do with one another . . . ."

On the contrary, practitioners of agriculture in the liberal arts see the liberal arts and the useful arts as complements. Each is capable of bringing something fresh to the study of the other. While they may be two cultures — the one more concerned with life's refreshment, the other with work's rewards — they need not be regarded as opposites incapable of cultural federation. The specific question before all is whether agriculture can join these two entities together, helping the one to recapture what it means to be liberally educated, and assisting the other to sense the full implications of actions taken in the name of practical necessity. The authors of chapters in this book believe that the answer in both respects is emphatically "yes."

The case for agriculture in the liberal arts is quite simple. First, the issues of agriculture are compellingly important: they resolve to the proper nourishment of the world's growing population for the indefinite future. There is no more important social problem in this century than the increasing imbalance between the human population and the resource base that sustains it. The problem is creeping, diffuse, and undramatic compared with others that command attention, such as nuclear proliferation, international monetary disturbances, or the politics of the Middle East. But few topics warrant fuller treatment in institutions dedicated to liberal objectives.

Fewer still provide so rich an opportunity to promote the goals of liberal learning. Thus, a second reason for encouraging the study of agriculture in the liberal arts is to help bring new coherence to the primary objectives of a liberal arts curriculum. Those objectives include nurturing an appreciation of the cultural legacy of human civilization; developing an awareness that knowledge itself is constantly changing and that it must be continuously questioned and renewed; developing the skills to make sound and responsible judgments; and fostering an informed concern for the fate of the species and the effect of new technologies.

Third, the study of agriculture in its several dimensions helps to focus many disciplines on a common object of study. Cross-disciplinary investigations are rare in modern academic life, especially when they involve disciplines with different methods of investigation. Yet the ease with which natural scientists, social scientists, and humanists have associated with one another in the experimental agriculture-in-the-liberal arts program is testimony to the potential for breaking down the barriers to understanding which fragment our educational institutions.

And fourth, explorations in agriculture can advance understanding of the linkage between thinking about an issue and experiencing the issue first hand. Too often institutionalized education presupposes, while at the same time blindly discourages, levels of experience, conceptual development, and motivation. Yet the most basic processes of learning are those which require people to use their personal experiences for understanding the information they receive. Several participants in the agriculture-in-the-liberal arts programs learned that agriculture and the natural world can be best understood when students mix their formal education with practical work experiences.

Lest you think this book is proposing the inclusion of courses on horticulture or animal husbandry in liberal arts curriculums, let us return to the second argument made above for studying aspects of agriculture in the liberal arts. Here are some illustrations of the kinds of insights that agriculture can provide institutions which are serious about developing a coherent, liberal arts curriculum.

At Pomona College, the steering committee of the Food, Land, and Power program identified four basic qualities a curriculum of liberal arts should develop in students. The first is an appreciation of the cultural legacy of human civilization. While courses in history, literature, anthropology, music, and art already deal with this subject in most liberal arts colleges, they generally give short shrift to the place of agriculture in human history. It is, after all, the activity most people have pursued for the last 3,000 years. Do you realize that little more than 100 years ago only one country in the world had succeeded in reducing the number of its citizens engaged in the production and distribution of food to less than half of the total population? Human history is primarily one of wrenching from nature enough food to survive; yet so little is said of this pervasive occupation that students are leaving college ignorant of their cultural taproot.

The second quality a liberal arts ought to instill in students is what Daniel Bell describes as the "grounds" of knowledge. "When a subject is presented as received doctrine or fact," Bell observes, "it becomes an aspect of specialization and technique. When it is introduced with an awareness of its contingency and of the conceptual frame that guides its organization, the student can then proceed with the necessary self-consciousness that keeps his or her mind open to possibility and to reorientation. All knowledge, thus, is liberal...when it is committed to continuing inquiry."[8]

Our understandings about agriculture are excellent illustrations of the changing nature of our knowledge. Consider, for example, that 10 years ago malnutrition was thought to reflect primarily a shortage of protein and, in some cases, vitamins or minerals. Yet today, based on more recent findings, most nutritional deficiencies are thought caused by a shortage of food rather than an imbalance between calories and protein. Thus, the most effective long-term policies to reduce malnutrition are those that raise the incomes of the poor and those that raise food production per person, especially in the developing world.

Or, consider the constantly shifting grounds for making judgments about the usefulness of particular agricultural techniques as the availability and uses of fossil energy shift, or as new insights about the sustainability of alternative agroecological systems are developed. Still again, consider the tentativeness of our policies to distribute food to the hungry in the Third World countries as new information emerges about the effects of alternative food distribution systems on the incentives of farmers to produce food locally, local food production, and as values shift in donor countries toward or against foreign aid.

Thirdly, the liberal arts also should cultivate a different attitude toward decision making. A liberally educated person must be prepared to make decisions that are not only technically correct, but responsible. Max Weber distinguishes between the "ethic of ultimate ends" and the "ethic of responsibility" in this regard. People following the first of these rules depend on received doctrine to guide them, and largely ignore the consequences of their actions. People who abide by the second ethic hold themselves responsible for the results of their actions. They, therefore, face the necessity from time to time of opposing the norms of accepted order to do the "right" thing. We believe a liberal arts education should help individuals to act according to the ethic of responsibility instead of the ethic of ultimate ends, and to understand the difference between the two.

Once again, agriculture provides rich illustrations of responsible (and irresponsible) decision making. Consider, for example, how two fundamental changes in U.S. agriculture — heightened specialization and increased internationalization — have altered the process of making responsible public decision about agriculture.

Specialization has changed the nature and focus of congressional constituency groups, which now are dominated by single-issue commodity interest. As a result, there no longer is a desire or mechanism for uniformity and consistency in commodity policies. In the executive branch of the federal government, moreover, the internationalization of agriculture has involved more people outside the agricultural community in policy-making.

Today, the State Department, the National Security Advisor, the U.S. Trade Representative, and sometimes even the Defense Department make agriculture-related decisions. This, of course, frustrates and angers farmers and their constituencies, the commodity groups, and much of the traditional commodity support in the Congress. New actors also have emerged to identify problems and develop policy solutions, in some ways reducing the importance of the land-grant universities in these processes. In short, the "public interest" is harder to define in the making of farm policy, and there is genuine worry about the prospect for making responsible farm policies when Congress considers major farm legislation in future years. Or consider, at the intensely personal level, how farmers make decisions every day which illustrate the choices between an ethic of ultimate ends (read short-term profit maximization) and the ethic of responsibility (read longer-term concern for the sustainability of nature's endowment).

Finally, the liberal arts ought to help students understand the changes which the United States and other peoples in the world are experiencing, and how, if left unattended, these trends and conditions may threaten our very survival. Nuclear war, population growth, material scarcity, and waste accumulation are extraordinarily complex problems. New technologies may offer hopeful solutions for aspects of these problems, but the potential for irresponsible uses of new techniques will be equally present.

Agriculture offers liberal arts institutions an excellent window on several of these problems. Evidence is mounting that food production per person is declining in some countries as soil erosion and other forms of biological stress occur. As these pressures mount, the worldwide effort to expand food production will lose momentum. In the process of trying to increase yields, moreover, the genetic base of many of the world's crops and livestock has been narrowed drastically. This makes them more vulnerable to pests and diseases and changes in soils and climate. Some 25,000 plant species and more than 1,000 vertebrate species and subspecies are now threatened with extinction, and as much as 10 percent or more of all species on earth could be extinguished over the next two decades. Extinction of species on this scale is without precedent in human history.

These four qualities — an appreciation of the cultural legacy of human civilization, an awareness that knowledge itself is contingent and must be questioned and renewed, an ability to make sound and responsible judgments, and an informed concern for the fate of the species and the effects of new technologies — represent key sources of inspiration for the liberal arts. An abiding concern for agriculture permits focused attention on these qualities, far more so than other themes or concerns which might be chosen to glue the liberal arts together.

Agriculture is basic to human welfare. It, more than other activities, has shaped our history and our culture. It is caught worldwide in a multidimensional crisis. Serious agricultural policy issues confront every country.

Because it is important and because the problems involved are complex, agriculture is an ideal subject for nurturing the intellectual qualities we associate with liberal learning. It is not the only subject which could animate the quest for these abiding qualities in students, but it surely is one of the best.

Program Elements

The programs described in Chapters 2 through 9 reveal the approaches different schools have adopted to build agricultural awareness in their faculties, student bodies, and communities. Some programs focused narrowly on agricultural concerns while others viewed agriculture in a broader environmental context. Some schools limited their fields of vision to regional or national issues whereas others took international agricultural development as their point of departure. The experimental programs differ also in the structure of disciplines chosen to anchor agricultural insights, though all schools explored agricultural linkages to the liberal arts in an intensely interdisciplinary way.

Curriculum

All schools concentrated their attention on innovations in the curriculum. Because the agriculture-in-the-liberal arts programs were designed to be compatible with the different structures and styles of host institutions, only some include broad survey courses, and only a couple have added specialized faculty members. Rather, in a majority of the experimental colleges, the principal methods of adding agricultural and environmental concerns to the curriculum have meant modifying existing courses, not creating new ones. Course modules on agriculture-related topics usually ranged between one-eighth and one-half of each modified course. In a few cases, the existence of one-unit minicourses in the regular curricular structure provided faculty and students with additional opportunities to tailor-make new course options.

Wholly new courses which were created in some institutions tend to be targeted on students seeking general rather than narrowly defined educational experiences. While some are team-taught, most have a single instructor.

None of the experimental colleges developed new student concentrations as a result of their experiment, although several permit individual students to construct special concentrations in agricultural or environmental studies under terms of existing faculty legislation. It should be noted that the possibility of developing a new student major is still a lively topic of discussion at more than one of the institutions.

After several years of experimentation, none of the colleges were able to create a "model" curriculum. Indeed, it may be fruitless to continue searching for one since student interests and modes of learning differ widely. Yet there are certain pieces of information which are so basic to agricultural literacy that serious consideration should be given to their integration into any curriculum. The list is still tentative, but it includes a description of the place of agriculture in human history; a philosophical investigation of the purposes of agriculture, with some attention to ethical considerations; and an examination of the links between nutrition and human development from the perspective of social science. It also includes a basic introduction to the biochemistry of agroecosystems; a comparative analysis of agricultural technologies, including an assessment of their impacts on ecological and social communities; a description of the institutions of political and economic power that shape agricultural decision in different societies; and a basic treatment of the demographic transition from higher to lower rates of population growth and the roles that the consumption and production of food play in that transition.

Public Events

All schools sponsored public events, ranging from lectures, films, and demonstrations to debates, colloquia, and conferences. Some of these events were cosponsored by other campus and off-campus organizations as a means of broadening audiences and building stronger links to community institutions. Since the styles and capacities of institutions to mount effective public events differ widely, it was learned that public events must be selected carefully to assure success. It was also discovered that students learn more from maximum exposure to outside experts. When special guests are invited to the campus to participate in public events, they should be encouraged to meet with classes and small groups as well.

Field Experiences

A third feature of some programs integrated personal experience into the educational process by letting students take a first-hand look at agriculture on nearby farms or arranging special internship programs for students away from the campus. Three of the experimental institutions own farms which permitted the construction of practicums for students otherwise enrolled in campus courses. Two others arranged summer internships away from home, and still another has developed a semester-long program which permits students to study traditional and modern agriculture side-by-side in a developing country.

These educational experiments are meant to bridge the gap between what is taught and what is learned through experience. In agriculture, as in other fields, truly informed decisions can be made only with a rich mixture of savvy and knowledgeability. Students learn concepts, theories, and descriptions of agricultural systems more quickly with hands-on experience. They also learn to question conventional wisdoms more readily at the site than they do at on-campus classes.

Other Activities

Several schools used the focus on agriculture in liberal arts to augment library resources. While a couple of schools embarked on an ambitious program of locating a model liberal arts holding of books and journals on agriculture and tried to replicate it, most schools adopted the practice of meeting the expressed needs of faculty members and students working in the field.

Some schools provided "Ag Hall" or "Vegehouse" group living arrangements for students, and several dedicated space for student-sponsored vegetable gardens. A few schools also worked hard at networking by establishing communication links with people at other institutions with like interests and by publishing a periodic newsletter containing program news, book lists and reviews, syllabi, essays, and calendars of national and regional events. One school developed an extension service to community groups interested in understanding some of the global issues with which the campus community is preoccupied, while several other institutions provided speakers on request for community groups.

Plans and Results

Now it is time to let leaders of the agriculture-in-the-liberal arts movement speak for themselves. In each of the following chapters, a person central to the design and implementation of a campus program — usually its director — reviews the origins and evolution of their campus leading to greater agricultural awareness. This is done by summarizing local perception of *The Problem* whose solution is sought and then by describing the institutional *Setting* which shapes and is shaped by the program. Each chapter's author then reviews the processes by which *Program Plans* were developed and an *Organization* was set in place to administer the program. The next section of most chapters, *Process and Products,* describes actual experience with the program and reveals the methods chosen to evaluate its results. Finally, each agriculture-in-the-liberal arts practitioner confesses the *Lessons Learned* in struggling to enhance the awareness of local constituencies about agriculture's myriad influences on our lives. In Chapter 10 of the book, attention is focused on the means of sustaining programmatic innovations after the excitement of initial efforts wanes and the supply of start-up resources is depleted.

Footnotes

[1]Aristotle, *Politics,* Benjamin Jowett (trans.) (Oxford: Clarendon Press, 1905) book 8, sec. 2, p. 301.

[2]Quoted from the *Edinburgh Review* in Martin J. Svaglic's introductory notes to John Henry Newman, *The Idea of a University* (San Francisco: Rinehard Press, 1960), p. xix.

[3]*Ibid,* pp. 115-116.

[4]Alfred North Whitehead, *The Aims of Education and Other Essays,* paperback ed. (New York: The Free Press, 1967), p. 94.

[5]*Ibid,* p. 96.

[6]For a fuller account of the shifting fortunes of the liberal and useful arts, see Earl F. Cheit, *The Useful Arts and the Liberal Tradition* (New York: McGraw-Hill, 1975).

[7]*Change in Liberal Education,* Association of American Colleges (Washington, D.C., 1973), p. 2.

[8]Daniel Bell, *The Reforming of a General Education* (New York: Columbia University Press, 1966), p. 8.

Chapter 2

Agriculture and the Environment
WILLIAMS COLLEGE
Williamstown, Massachusetts

Thomas C. Jorling

The Problem

From 1972 to 1975 a frequent topic of discussions at Williams College's Center for Environmental Studies was agriculture and its relationship to the College. These discussions were stimulated by student and faculty concern over the 1973 oil embargo, a growing population, the importance of agribusiness to the economy, the need for ecological awareness in managed ecosystems, and soil erosion and natural resource losses. Emerging from these talks was a growing awareness that there was an obvious void in the College's curriculum, both in courses focusing specifically on agriculture issues and the integration of these topics within existing courses. Also, faculty and students became cognizant that, over the years, the Williams' student body had changed from predominantly rural in background to one with urban and suburban roots.

Consequently, students had little first-hand experience with, or exposure to, the living systems on which human communities depend. In addition, the discussions revealed an intellectual arrogance toward agricultural topics existed at the College. Another problem unmasked was that graduates of Williams College were ill-equipped to be leaders of our society; they had little or no understanding of the agricultural basis of the nation and world at large.

Recognizing that issues related to food production are central to any serious inquiry into the human predicament, the College concluded that they "needed to do something" to focus attention

Thomas C. Jorling is director of the Center for Environmental Studies at Williams College, Williamstown, MA.

on the role of agriculture in our society. That something was a proposal to the W. K. Kellogg Foundation to support the introduction of agriculture into the Williams' curriculum and community.

The Setting

Williams College is a small (@1900 students) liberal arts college situated in rural northwestern Massachusetts. The Center for Environmental Studies is an interdisciplinary educational unit within the College. It is administered by an advisory committee comprised of individuals from 10 different academic units of the College. The existence of the Center and its advisory committee was instrumental in all phases of the Kellogg program, especially in generating support among the faculty members and administrative personnel for explicitly introducing agriculture to Williams. Perhaps, fortuitously, the committee's membership included some highly respected faculty members. This not only provided secure footing for the Center for Environmental Studies, it enabled full and enthusiastic support to develop within the College and administration for the agriculture proposal.

In retrospect, the ability to go forward with the agriculture program was helped — perhaps even made possible — by several factors. These included the presence of: a preexisting interdisciplinary program — the Center for Environmental Studies — with ties throughout the academic and administrative structures of the College. There also was a predisposition and explicit policy within Williams College supporting interdisciplinary programs (History of Ideas, Area Studies, American Civilization, Afro-American Studies); an administration, drawn primarily from faculty members determined to, in the words of the dean of faculty, "assist interdisciplinary programs in reaching their place in the sun"; and an openness to new and innovative ideas within the College community.

In preparing the proposal, the geographical setting of Williams College played a distinct role. Although much surrounding agricultural land had been abandoned, Williamstown and nearby Massachusetts, Vermont, and New York communities had active agricultural enterprises — predominantly dairy operations — that could be drawn on for actual hands-on educational and research activity.

Some elements of the setting, however, were more limiting. While the support of the Kellogg Foundation oriented hiring decisions and stimulated redirection of faculty interest, the success of the effort was necessarily dependent on existing faculty resources and interests. Not surprisingly, only a limited number of faculty members at Williams College were interested in and knowledgeable about agriculture. Secondly, and typical of most liberal arts institutions, there was a serious deficiency in the availability of agricultural literature. Thirdly, the course approval process of the College operated "out of sync" with the grant proposal. This caused a chicken-and-egg type of problem. Approximately one year passed after the grant was awarded in 1976 before the first full courses were added to the curriculum.

Program Plan

An analysis of the opportunities and limitations of the setting, as described above, provided the shape and structure for the actual proposal to the Kellogg Foundation for implementation of an agriculture-in-the-liberal arts program. The objectives of the proposal fell into three categories: the addition of courses to the curriculum, the acquisition of library and associated materials, and the generation of interest and enthusiasm for agricultural matters within and around Williams College.

Courses:

The program at Williams attempted three curricular changes. The most ambitious was the addition of two regular semester courses — one with a historical/cultural orientation rooted in the arts and humanities and another designed to examine the energetics and dynamics (the ecology) of contemporary agriculture emphasizing science. The second curricular development was a range of Winter Study offerings related to agriculture. Winter Study is a month-long period during which students enroll in only one, three-credit course. The course allows unconventional pedagogical structure and function, including travel, and is a unique educational opportunity for concentrated, often experiential learning. The third curricular change was the addition of agriculture components to existing courses throughout the College, specifically in economics, political science, biology, and history. More than one-half the resources sought from Kellogg were for these functions.

Library Materials:

Books, research reports, government documents, and journals on such topics as agricultural history, economics, and policy were added to the library materials at Williams College. This was accomplished by building on and using the resources of the Environmental Studies Library. While this initially included one-time acquisitions, most subscriptions for the journals obtained with Foundation support have been continued. Less than one-quarter of the resources requested were earmarked for the acquisition of library materials.

Community Interest:

The objective to generate interest, support, and enthusiasm for the overall introduction of agriculture into the Williams community was considered paramount to the success of the program. Consequently, a definitive set of activities directed at generating such support were established at the onset of the program. These included the featuring of guest lecturers and other appropriate visitors; the conduct of field trips and symposia; and the securement of research support. Williams College also attempted to remain alert to other opportunities for cultivating support and interest in agricultural topics and issues. About one-quarter of the resources solicited for the College's agriculture-in-the-liberal arts programs were for this purpose.

Program Organization

The Center for Environmental Studies which, for all practical and functional purposes, is an academic department in Williams College, was and continues to be responsible for the execution of the program. The incorporation of the agriculture program into this existing structure and function greatly facilitated the program's management and conduct.

In addition to serving as the administrative mechanism for the grant, the Center for Environmental Studies provided a policy forum for the project. The Center's advisory committee handled such functions as the review and modification of new and existing course syllabi. It also coordinated the agriculture-in-the-liberal arts courses and their administration by the College's various departments, thereby helping to minimize disciplinary "turf" concerns.

In addition, the Center provided support staff assistance to the project. Individuals handled arrangements for visitors, guest speakers, and public events. They dealt with local farmers too.

Establishing relationships with farmers was especially rewarding. Extensive site visits to farms, including "hands-on" learning and work experience was very successful. Farmers' "real world" explanations of dairy supports, co-op marketing, and escalating machinery needs, for instance, were worth weeks in the classroom.

Process and Product

During the grant period all basic and formal objectives were met: two full semester courses were added; a competent collection of library materials was acquired; and numerous, often exciting, events and persons were hosted by the College.

While the program was generally successful, several elements of the program disappointed the most ardent backers of the pilot effort. One of the most bothersome was the program's history of attracting only a limited number of students to course offerings. Debriefings and post hoc reviews indicated several reasons for this. Among the most important was that the courses satisfied no departmental or distributional requirement for any major. Thus, many students who might have been interested in the offerings would not or could not enroll in such a 'purely' elective course.

Secondly, the courses were not firmly fixed in class schedules. Often they were listed in registration material as "to be announced." This occurred because the College had problems securing teachers for the classes. (Small college faculties share some inherent limitations when it comes to offering new courses which are neither part of a traditional department nor courses required of a traditional major. Essentially, a faculty person, even one who is interested, is only free to participate in a new offering after required departmental course offerings are staffed and leaves are covered. Hiring decisions follow the same pattern. Thus matching the staff to the course at the right time can be difficult at best, and frustrating at worst.)

Winter Study offerings, on the other hand, tended to be over-subscribed, and there was frequently a regret that more offerings could not have been made available. Winter Study courses provided the greatest range of interaction of faculty and students with members of the local agricultural community. In addition, the winter courses enabled students to visit different institutions and sites in various parts of the country in all sectors of agricultural enterprise. These included commodity markets, food processing plants, as well as all kinds and scales of farm and ranch operations. These courses provided many Williams College students with their first exposure to the work-a-day world of agriculture. While helping the students learn first-hand about agriculture, the Winter Study courses heightened respect among Williams students for those engaged in agricultural production, processing, and distribution.

The selection and acquisition of library materials also moved along smoothly. Cataloging and filing of the materials was handled jointly by the College's staff and historian. Both worked to organize the materials in the library so they would be accessible to all, particularly to individuals researching agricultural topics. A common sense solution was followed. This included establishing a separate heading and location for agricultural materials and cross-indexing the material in the appropriate catalog. For instance, all literature related to agricultural economics was listed under agricultural economics and then cross-indexed under economics.

The most visible and widely acclaimed component of the program was the conduct of activities to introduce the local community to the field of agriculture. These events included symposia, festivals, field trips, and the like. Among the more successful of these events were those centering on the Hopkins Forest Farm Museum, located at the College's Hopkins Forest. Generally these festivals focused on specific themes, such as raising sheep or maple sugaring, and they involved local farmers. More academically oriented forums included panel discussions with scholars and farmers on subjects such as agricultural land ownership and tax policy. These events provided great insight into the complicated array of factors influencing current agricultural dynamics.

Care was taken by Williams College to involve as many departments of the College as possible in the events. Thus, if an agricultural economist or business person was going to be invited to speak on campus, a representative of the Economics Department was asked to serve as co-host to the event. Project personnel believed that isolation of the agricultural program in the liberal arts college would surely doom the project.

Generally, the agricultural program at Williams influenced students in one of three ways. First, approximately six students directed their energies and future career paths toward agriculture as a result of the program. The second group of students, the bulk of those enrolling in the agriculture-in-the-liberal arts program, gained a serious appreciation and understanding of agriculture and its role in society, though not to the extent of changing their basic career plans. This was the outcome specifically sought for the program. The third group of students, which was very small, simply were not affected by the program and its offerings.

The impact on faculty, as might be expected, was less pervasive. The program did not reach, or if it did reach, did not cause much change among faculty not otherwise interested in agricultural subjects. Nevertheless, those members of the faculty involved in the program, and by definition already predisposed to agriculture and its importance, gained an opportunity to systematically expand their interest and orientation. Because of this sustained faculty interest in agriculture, Williams College has continued to offer its two agriculture-in-the-liberal arts courses on an alternate-year basis as part of its overall College curriculum.

Perhaps the greatest, and most unanticipated benefit of the program was the penetration of barriers between the local agricultural community and the College community. The reality behind Jefferson's description of farming as "the first in utility, and ought to be the first in respect" was made clear when, for instance, a dairy farmer described the variables of every day agriculture: feeds, breeding, disease, production, marketing, planting, growing, harvesting, and the vagaries of weather. Even the most sophisticated of students were refreshed with some humility; not just at the work burden, but more by the knowledge required to engage in agriculture.

Similarly, the local community realized College folks are not totally oblivious to practical problems and the vagaries of living systems. These discoveries were mutually rewarding.

Even friendships of durability were established between local farmer and student, and faculty and farmer.

Lessons Learned

If results of the program are measured by the specific objectives initially established by the effort, then Williams College's agriculture-in-the-liberal arts program was a success. However, it may not have succeeded in making more than a passing dent in the overall tradition or attitude of a liberal arts college. Agriculture still is perceived by a great number of people as foreign to and generally unwelcome by the liberal arts.

Because liberal arts colleges tend to be small, innovation frequently is dependent on existing faculty interest and energy. Consequently, faculty leaves and turnover can disrupt a program. It is difficult to replace people with similar interest and skills when such qualifications are secondary to the basic needs of the institution. Certainly the Williams program suffered from this type of occurrence.

Perhaps the most fundamental lesson learned is the need for grantmaking institutions — such as foundations — to take into account the long-term implications of supporting the introduction of innovations in higher education institutions. Sometimes even the most successful programs cannot be picked up by the institutions at the end of the grant period because of limited financial resources. The Williams College experience strongly suggests that foundation support of a scaled-down project at the outset, followed by support for an endowment or a small concluding grant would have greater payoff. Without such aid the legacy of the agriculture programs may vanish as the faculty who have ties back to the original grant disappear.

Chapter 3

Agriculture in the Liberal Arts

EARLHAM COLLEGE
Richmond, Indiana

James V. McDowell

The Problem

Earlham College's agriculture-in-the-liberal arts program was the brainchild of a group of students concerned about food production, transportation, and consumption problems. The students reasoned that to understand how domestic and international events affect agriculture they needed to participate in small-scale agricultural projects with tangibly relevant academic work in the liberal arts curriculum. With conspicuous enthusiasm and resolve to bring such a study program into reality, the students approached the College's administration and faculty for assistance and direction.

In 1977 a proposal for funds to initiate an agriculture-in-the-liberal arts program was prepared jointly by College administrators, faculty, and students. The effort was funded by the W. K. Kellogg Foundation as part of a strategy to introduce agriculture education into selected liberal arts colleges throughout the nation.

Goals of the Earlham College effort were to:

increase the knowledge and awareness of all students and faculty members concerning agricultural policy issues, including those faculty members whose courses bear on agriculture policy;

increase critical awareness and knowledge of intermediate technology in agriculture among faculty and students;

encourage and provide practical experience in agriculture and in agricultural research and development;

make students aware of career possibilities in agriculture-related fields; and

encourage students interested in graduate agricultural science studies to pursue an appropriate major in one of the natural sciences.

James V. McDowell is professor emeritus of psychology at Earlham College, Richmond, IN.

The Setting

The Kellogg grant proposal assessed and determined the type of higher educational environment in which such informed persons might be prepared. It stated:

It seems clear . . . that conventional agricultural science programs at large universities cannot meet this need. Rarely will there be the degree of integration across disciplines called for, and perhaps even more rarely will students from other fields elect agricultural programs to broaden their knowledge in chosen liberal arts fields. It is equally clear that the traditional liberal arts program, even with the more recent environmental focus, is not adequate. What is needed is a program clearly focused on agricultural studies, with stronger experiential learning components, which is well integrated into a variety of liberal arts fields.

The proposal argued further that a program in agricultural studies integrated with traditional liberal arts subjects required two special elements which were firmly present at Earlham College. First, it must have the ability to generate and maintain the appropriate interdisciplinary courses in a program of study. Earlham had demonstrated this ability by developing such interdisciplinary courses and cross-disciplinary programs of study as its Human Development and Social Relations program and its Peace and Conflict Studies program (now the Peace and Global Studies program). Further, a pilot course designed to introduce agricultural studies was designed by a group of students and faculty for the 1978-79 school year.

The second element needed was the proper physical and faculty resources. The Earlham campus itself was located on the site of two pioneer farms. Today the College owns more than 600 acres of prime farm land adjacent to its campus with the major part being tilled by a tenant farmer. It also operates a 35-acre farm known as Miller Farm. Until the 1950s, a number of students took part-time work in farming and dairy operations of the College, though this activity had no formal linkage to the College's academic program. A program in agricultural science was launched in 1951, but was discontinued shortly thereafter in the face of other competing liberal arts majors.

The new agriculture-in-the-liberal arts program, the proposal affirmed, was designed to overcome mistakes of the past. The program would neither be set up as an adjunct to the College's existing educational program nor would it be established as a separate competing major in a traditional liberal arts environment.

Program Plan

To what student constituencies was the agriculture-in-the-liberal arts program addressed? While the program's objectives suggested that the pilot effort was intended to increase knowledge, awareness, and critical thought about agriculture across the whole spectrum of the student body and the faculty, the grant proposal zeroed in on three specific student groups. Those groups included:

1. Students preparing to become farmers, agricultural scientists, or workers in food processing industries. These students would major in a related discipline, such as biology or economics, with an additional concentration in the agricultural studies program. (Initially this group was estimated to be small.)

2. Students interested in doing personal, paravocational, small-scale gardening or food production along with another major occupation.

   This group would encompass individuals majoring in a variety of other fields, with a concentration in agricultural studies. (This group was thought to be several times larger than the first group and was expected to grow in size in the future.)

3. Students majoring in any liberal arts discipline wishing to develop a second focus through a series of courses satisfying Earlham's liberal arts distribution requirements. (This group would include a majority of the students in the College.)

The program was designed with three chief components: contributing academic courses, student-conducted small farm activities, and summer internships. During the Kellogg grant period there also was a series of visiting lecturers and consultants and a stipend program to enable faculty to prepare agricultural-related courses and course components.

Academic Courses

The academic component of the program consisted primarily of regular liberal arts courses that had some content concerned with food and agriculture. For example, a course on violence and world order dealt with international transactions relating to food; a course on energy, technology, and human affairs considered energy use with different agricultural methods and involved the study of applications of energy to food processing and the heating of buildings; an introductory course in philosophy examined food ethics and food policy issues. Agricultural-related components usually ranged from one-fifth to one-half of the course. Some 12 such courses were offered in the years 1978 through 1981. Departments involved were: biology, chemistry, economics, geology, philosophy, physics, political science, and sociology-anthropology.

Only one course was designed solely for purposes of the agriculture-in-the-liberal arts program. Entitled Agriculture Living/Learning, it provided a close integration between the study of scientific topics and practical experience in small-scale agriculture at a nearby farm. The course was designed jointly by interested faculty and a group of students, and was offered in 1978-80. Discontinued in the face of considerable faculty criticism and for lack of available teachers, the course was replaced in the fall of 1981 by Ecology of Agriculture, a more explicitly scientific course to which Ecological Biology was a prerequisite. This course was discontinued a year later because no College department felt in a position to allot the faculty time and energy needed to mount the course another year. The small number of students successfully completing the course — 6 of 12 who began it — also had a bearing upon this outcome. While the possibility remains that the course, or a lineal successor to it, might be offered at a future time, there is no immediate plan to do so.

Since the end of the 1981 school year, several other courses have been discontinued. These include:

Department	Course
Chemistry	Basic Nutrition
Geology	Soil Science
Interdepartmental	Habitat: Land Use and the Human Prospect

Further, the discussion/lab section of the Ecological Biology course, offered in 1980-81, was dropped. The academic part of the program has been reduced to eight courses in six departmental areas. They are as follows:

Department	Course	Comments
Biology	Ecological Biology	
	Entomology	Offered in alternate years
	Plants & Human Affairs	Offered in alternate years
Economics	Principles of Economy II	Continuation of ag-related content now under consideration
Philosophy	Intro. to Philosophy II: Food Ethics	
Physics	Energy, Technology, and Human Affairs	
Spanish	Mexican Culture	
Interdepartmental	Kenya Study Program	

There remains some uncertainty about the viability of the agricultural component of the economics course. The course instructor is deliberating on whether other content areas might be more timely and appropriate for illustration of economic concepts.

Apparent reasons for discontinuation of these efforts were: small student enrollments, loss of faculty members who had been specially qualified and interested in teaching the courses, and the necessity to reduce course offerings due to reductions in faculty.

Interestingly, most of the discontinued courses were in the science field. This suggests that interest in scientific studies relevant to agriculture was not widespread. It hints at an overall lack of student interest in the study of science as well. (This is particularly true of students living at Miller Farm; seldom have these individuals been science majors.)

Student-Conducted Activities

To date, student-conducted activities have centered on the 35-acre Miller Farm, which is a mile and a half from the main campus and provides house accommodations for nine students. The resident students are responsible for maintaining the Farm's garden, a flock of chickens, a few bee hives, a small nursery of fruit and nut seedlings, a wood-stove heating operation, and a greenhouse. They receive help from other students in periodic work projects — these students come principally from Ag Hall, a 22-member dormitory unit on the main campus that serves to recruit and orient new participants in Miller Farm activities and to promote agricultural-related public events on campus.

Students reportedly are pleased with the hands-on experience provided to them at Miller Farm. Recent interviews with five resident students at Miller Farm showed strong student support for keeping the farm going, recruiting a continuing supply of future active residents, and continuing educational activity within the College's student body.

Miller Farm had somewhat strained relations with the Housing Office in 1982-83 over questions concerning student occupancy during vacations and care of animals over the summer. But these issues have been resolved by the designation of a student of proven responsibility and availability to look after the Miller Farm plant and livestock when other students are away.

Internships

The internship component of the agriculture-in-the-liberal arts program initially entailed three projects which involved up to 12 students. In the summer of 1980 the projects were as follows:

The Meeting School Project, Rindge, New Hampshire: Students conducted ecologically oriented gardening and animal care, participated in food preservation activities, and conducted individual, supervised projects. (Four interns.)

The Small Farm Energy Project, Hartington, Nebraska: Participants helped organize and teach workshops on reducing dependence on fossil fuels. They also built and installed solar devices on farms. (One intern.)

Mexican Friends Service Committee: Students received language instruction and orientation from governmental agriculture specialists and then worked on rural village agricultural projects. They also taught French intensive gardening, a means of obtaining remarkably high food production from small areas of land, to school children. (Four interns.)

Students usually took the internships on a no-credit basis. However, they could receive one credit by designating their internship as Independent Study. This entailed substantial related academic work that had to be approved in advance and supervised by an Earlham faculty member.

By the end of 1981-82, only one internship project continued to be active: placement with the Mexican Friends Service Committee. Three to four students participated in the effort during the summers of 1981, '82, and '83. None participated in 1984 due to temporary circumstances.

Miscellaneous Activities

Another significant component of the program was the agricultural-related activities. These included:

the conduct of on-campus lectures on food and agriculture topics by 13 visiting resource people who also met with classes and served as consultant for the program;

student participation in outside workshops and conferences (for example, in 1981 a group of students attended a conference/workshop in Kentucky on small farm practices);

student production and distribution of *Cornstalk,* a mimeographed newsletter which reported on agriculture-in-the-liberal arts program activities, reviewed books on agriculture, and commented on agricultural topics (this publication did not appear during the 1982-83 school year; one issue was printed in the fall of 1984);

the provision of career guidance literature, group guidance sessions, and individual counseling by the College's Career Planning and Placement Office; and

the granting of stipends to faculty who make special preparation to teach courses or course components addressed to problems of agriculture (of 13 teachers who offered agriculture-in-the-liberal arts courses, 10 received such stipends in the first four years of the program).

Program Organization

Two agencies were initially responsible for the pilot effort. A joint faculty-student steering committee conducted general planning, budgetary control, and handled relationships involving the faculty and administration. Under direction of the steering committee, a faculty member responsible to the dean of the faculty served part-time as director of the program during the Kellogg grant period. In addition, a part-time administrative assistant helped operate the program. When the College assumed full financial responsibility for takeover of the agriculture-in-the-liberal arts program, the administrative assistant position was terminated. A joint faculty-student steering committee continues to exercise supervision over the program.

The second agency was comprised of students. It was responsible for working out the specifics of operating Miller Farm and for developing proposals to be submitted to the steering committee. That group continues to operate today. (Ag Hall, mentioned earlier, operates autonomously within the framework of College housing arrangements, in mutually supportive liaison with students at Miller Farm.)

Process and Product

To evaluate program outcomes, questionnaires were distributed to 66 students in six agriculture-in-the-liberal arts courses. In the questionnaires, Earlham College probed to find out how students responded to the agricultural-related components in their courses. (Throughout the study it was kept in mind that the majority of students had enrolled in the courses not because of their relevance to agriculture but simply because the courses were a part of the student's regular nonagricultural program.)

With only one exception, the students considered the agricultural components of each course as valuable or more valuable an educational experience than other parts of the courses. This was true regardless of the degree of interest in agriculture with which they entered the course. Three-fourths of the students reported that their interest in agriculture had increased through the course; none said it had decreased.

To sample the views of students explicitly interested in the agriculture-in-the-liberal arts program, students who had engaged in experiential components of the program were interviewed. Their views reflected each individual's distinctive pattern of interest and involvement. For one, the high point of agricultural experience was practice in organizing and directing the work of others. For another, who alleged she came to Earlham having no notion of what a piece of pork was before it appeared in the supermarket wrapped in cellophane, it was learning the basic facts and skills related to agriculture. This led gradually to her resolving to learn as much as she could about the whole agricultural system, including scientific studies which hitherto had "terrified" her, economic and intercultural ramifications that attracted her, and related agricultural arts and crafts which had interested her. For still another it was a deepening of understanding and skills that had begun in an earlier broad exposure to farming.

Themes frequently expressed by students were:

Tie-ins between academic studies and practical experiences. Said one: "The nitrogen cycle became meaningful for me when I figured out how the compost pile (at Miller Farm) worked." Another, thinking of majoring in philosophy, found agriculture "the basis of civilization" around which to sort out his thinking on politics, science, economics, and cultural values. Several reported writing papers relating to agriculture as parts of their coursework. A sophomore said, "More and more I find myself relating topics in my other courses to agriculture. For example, in a European history course, I did an individual project on collective farms in East Germany."

Development of self-understanding and social skills. Several said they gained respect for the differing views of others, acquired an ability to listen to others and work with them toward group consensus, and obtained a sense of responsibility to the group (at Miller Farm) for doing chores and keeping the place running smoothly. (Two faculty people noted student gains in group decision-making skills and in understanding how the college bureaucracy operates. They felt these accomplishments were outstanding.)

Friendships and sense of social support.

Broader grasp of the worldwide problems of food and agriculture. In the words of one student, "I see ag/food/environment problems much more in the perspective of the world, international relations, a whole interrelated package of things. Perhaps I'd have seen this anyhow, but it came through vividly in the agriculture-in-the-liberal arts program."

Development in career plans and preparation. Several participants decided (tentatively or firmly) on the use of small-scale agriculture as a vehicle in community organization or teaching. At least two students came to Earlham with the intention of transferring to colleges of agriculture and explored that idea further through the program. Several alumni reported being involved in activities for which agriculture-in-the-liberal arts program provided a valuable base of experience. Among these were: organizing farmer markets, conducting part-time or full-time farming, working in food cooperatives, and pursuing the full-time study of agriculture. One alumnus received a scholarship toward a doctorate in social economy and social policy. Her particular interest, which developed partially as a result of her summer intern experience with the Mexican Friends Service Committee, is agriculture in the Third World. Another alumnus completed doctoral study in agricultural economics, and still another is in a doctoral program in plant physiology.

Earlham College inquired also into faculty views of program outcomes, primarily through interviews with teachers of agriculture-in-the-liberal arts courses. All 13 of those interviewed supported the idea of integrating agriculture into a liberal arts curriculum and felt Earlham was an appropriate place for doing so. They characteristically favored the "spirit" of the program but expressed reservations about various aspects of the effort. These centered around student tendencies toward practical and lifestyle interests which they viewed as being counter to academic thoroughness; student preferences for organic and small-scale approaches which interfered with objective, fact-oriented inquiry; insufficient communication about the program to the college community at large, especially before submission of the proposal for a grant; and uncertainty about the overall impact of the program, though recognizing its significance and influence on a number of students involved.

Many of the misgivings appeared to derive from early impressions concerning the heavily practicum-oriented, student-planned Agriculture Living/Learning course that was replaced in the fall term of 1981 by Ecology of Agriculture. Some faculty thought it was not feasible within the bounds of a single introductory course to develop sufficient depth of scientific understanding to deal with the questions. Others thought that student influence over course content and methods had been excessive.

As to personal experiences in teaching agriculture-in-the-liberal arts-contributing courses, faculty members reported that their learning experiences in preparing to teach the agricultural-related course components (for which 10 of the 13 received stipends) were valuable. They also said they felt pleased about the agriculture-related components after teaching them. Most indicated that they did not change teaching methods because of the program, rather they changed some of their course content.

Lessons Learned

The following conclusions were drawn from the preponderance of people who have been associated with the program at Earlham College, including students, faculty, and administrators:

Students most likely to be attracted to the program are those drawn to agriculture as an avocation and those attracted to country living as a preferred lifestyle. In relation to the broad field of agriculture and food supply, students are interested primarily in agriculture's socioeconomic and ethical aspects rather than its scientific side, and, as a rule, do not maintain it as a vocational focus.

The provision of speakers on food and agriculture and the conduct of conferences and promotional drives (e.g., World Hunger Days) are critical to program development.

Success of the program depends on the desire and choice of individual faculty members to take part in the effort. Let that interest be diverted and the academic part of the program will simply fade out.

Stipends to faculty members to prepare agricultural-related courses provide valuable experiences in professional development.

The partial-subsistence small-farm project is a remarkably appealing and productive student activity. It fosters individual social growth and competence in working with a group, intellectual stimulation, responsibility, competence in administrative tasks, and vocational development. In the eyes of the students, the project appears to be the center of the program's energy and activity.

Clearly, Earlham College's agriculture-in-the-liberal arts program has proven that it is feasible to develop a multipurpose program concerning food and agriculture within the structure and style of a strongly academic, liberal arts college. Such a program can strengthen the knowledge and concern of a considerable number of students and faculty about relevant policy and scientific issues. It can provide training and experience in practical skills and knowledge, especially as related to small-scale farming. In addition, it has the potential to enhance awareness of career and avocational possibilities relating to food and agriculture. Such possibilities range from natural science, social science, and managerial work to plans emphasizing rural life-style and personal involvement in food production.

Chapter 4

The Consortium on Agriculture and World Hunger

Four Iowa Colleges

OVERVIEW

Harland S. Nelson

To get to the four Iowa colleges in the Consortium on Agriculture and World Hunger — Coe, Cornell, Grinnell, and Luther — students drive through some of the richest farmland in the United States. Even a generation ago, a large proportion of them would have known from personal experience what working in those fields and on those farmsteads was like, and would have been pretty clear about where the food they loaded their cafeteria trays with came from.

But, as Glenn I. Nelson, professor of sociology and then academic vice president at Luther College, wrote in his 1980 proposal to the Kellogg Foundation, the rapid urbanizing of the United States since World War II has meant that Iowa colleges, in spite of their location, now have far fewer students from farms and farm villages than they used to. Similarly, fewer members of their faculties are likely to know anything about farming. The consequence, he concluded, "has been a higher education enterprise [whose faculty] lacks insight into current agriculture, while serving a group of students who have only the most limited knowledge of this subject." The potential effect for society is serious: tomorrow's leaders coming out of these colleges will know far less about the real significance of agriculture, in the United States and in the rest of the world, than they need to.

None of these colleges, of course, sends many graduates directly into agriculture, though some of them go back to work in the family farm enterprises that they were a part of before they

---

Harland S. Nelson is professor of English and director of the Consortium on Agriculture and World Hunger, Luther College, Decorah, IA.

entered college. But sending more graduates into farming was not the goal of the four colleges when they formed the Consortium on Agriculture and World Hunger; the goal was to keep on sending graduates where they are going now, better able to understand the importance of a thriving and sustainable agriculture, and better equipped and motivated to recognize and act upon opportunities for promoting it.

When the Consortium began its three-year life in February 1981, the blueprint was Glenn Nelson's proposal to the Foundation. Accordingly, the students at the four colleges were the target audience, and the design therefore included curricular development and student orientation. There was also a provision for events reaching out to the communities beyond the campuses, not only because such events are valuable in themselves but because the attention they command among people outside the college authenticates those agricultural concerns to students. And finally, the design provided for faculty development. The main vehicle for this was to be a three-week summer seminar.

The life of the Consortium has been close to what Glenn Nelson envisioned. The Consortium has carried out a cycle of events each year, beginning with the summer seminar held at Luther College for a dozen faculty members from the four colleges (a different set each summer). Through the following academic year these teachers planned and presented on their home campuses a fall workshop for other faculty, and spring and fall symposiums on specific topics of current interest for the entire on- and off-campus community. In the classroom, they have worked what they learned at the seminar into their existing courses where possible. For students interested in following up topics on agriculture or world food questions on their own, there has been provision for independent study. Also, the teachers who have attended the summer seminars are developing or have developed for adoption into their own college's curriculum a regular semester course (most likely interdisciplinary) dealing with agriculture and food production. To support this academic activity each Consortium college library has received $2,000 a year to add appropriate books, periodicals, and audiovisual materials. (This infusion of funds is broadly useful as well to many of the regular departments of instruction in their traditional offerings and activities.) One other aim of the Consortium — to develop a component of the orientation for new students at each college to acquaint them with the agricultural locale — has not gone well; what I have to say about that appears near the end of this report.

The philosophy of the Consortium, as this brief sketch of its parts suggests, has been to make awareness of farming and the world's food needs a part of what liberally educated students take with them from their formal studies into their lives and careers. Thus, while the Consortium provides for visibility in the curriculum (the regular semester course), it does not propose to generate majors in agriculture or developmental studies, or even clusters of Consortium courses. It hopes to give students a glimpse of what their teachers had opened to them in the seminars; the structure of modern agriculture, and the way modern farming is done (including some awareness of the capital investment involved); land use; the influence of public policy on farm production and trade in farm products; the infrastructure that supports farming; the significance of exports for U.S. farming; the dimensions of world food needs, and the proportion to be met in national needs by imports; nutrition; the interconnection of agricultural development and general economic policy; and possible alternatives to present structures and methods of operation. While this looks like mostly nuts and bolts, it reflects our belief that students at liberal arts colleges are likely to know nothing, or nearly nothing, about farming and food production. They are likely to be characterized most noticeably by their humanitarian motives and by the guilt that well-disposed affluent people feel about their luck. The job is to infuse all that with some reality, so that the generous impulses do not go to waste. We try to make students aware of agricultural matters. Since we are not developing a major, this seems both enough to do, and worth doing.

But elsewhere, in our own disciplines, in courses we have been teaching and continue to teach, we look for ways to incorporate our new knowledge and concerns. As any teacher knows, there are moments every day in any liberal arts course — physics, economics, history, literature — when connections with agriculture are possible and appropriate to any topic the teacher knows and cares about. That is how the Consortium has been making its daily, unspectacular, incremental effect: not by educating a corps of experts on each campus, not by setting up a new academic preserve where students can go who have somehow become interested in the field and want to specialize in it. The idea has been to make it likely that they will run across this material no matter what they major in.

The Summer Seminar

The most important part of the Consortium for making all this happen — all participants agree about this — has been the three-week summer seminar held at Luther College. The seminars have included a week of sessions on selected topics led by consultants from universities, foundations devoted to agricultural and food production concerns, and agribusinesses; followed by a week of visiting farms and agribusinesses in east central Iowa (there is nothing like two hours jammed into a 15-passenger van driving past miles of corn and soybeans for generating agricultural conversation among professors of the liberal arts); and concluded with another week of consultant-led seminar sessions.

A substantial list of advance readings for general background has been given to all summer seminar participants. The readings have included, from the beginning, *A Time to Choose: Summary Report on the Structure of Agriculture* (1981), intended as a prelude to the reform of government agricultural policy when it was commissioned by President Carter's secretary of agriculture Bob Bergland; and a 1980 collection of articles on the state of world food production published in the journal, *Society,* under the editorship of Vernon Ruttan, professor of agricultural economics at the University of Minnesota. These basic readings have been augmented each year by new articles on various topics, and consultants also have recommended readings (amounting in sum to a considerable bibliography) appropriate to their particular sessions. (See Appendix III.)

We used a total of 21 consultants in the three seminars. Only three worked in two seminars, and only two took part in all three. Thus the seminars differed considerably in detail. Consultants included a University of Minnesota agricultural economist on the evolution of agricultural technologies; a University of Wisconsin agronomist on his work with rice farmers in the Philippines; and Iowa State University nutritionist on cultural and economic factors affecting nutrition in developing countries; a Cargill executive on the complexities of international grain markets; a rural affairs specialist on the transformation of rural life by technological development since World War II; a soil scientist on the threat of erosion to a sustainable agriculture; a political scientist on the politics of agricultural research and government policy; and a veteran agricultural observer and reporter on the design of a more rational policy for agriculture. (See Appendix IV for a complete list of consultants and topics.)

Field trips have taken participants to research farms operated by a feed company, fructose and alcohol production facilities, a seed company's experimental plot; and to different kinds of farms — contemporary examples of the "family farm" growing field crops, raising hogs, producing milk; a successful organic farm; and the 25,000-acre Amana colony farms, different from the others in important ways deriving from the communal system of ownership, as well as from different values.

What the three summer sessions have produced is a core of three dozen faculty, 8 to 10 from each college, who carry on Consortium work on their respective campuses. They vary in age from the 30s to the late 50s, they include men and women (though men outnumber women four to one), and they represent disciplines across the liberal arts. This mix ensures interdisciplinary structure of program, and stability through time. And the evolution of the seminar over three years means that while participants have a great deal of common experience, each year's cadre has something to learn from the other two. The critical thing, of course, is whether anything significant has happened to these people. On that score their opinion is unanimous: something has happened. Several of them, in independent evaluation of their experience later on, have said much the same thing: they now find themselves noticing, reading, and understanding (so far as anyone can claim to understand) the issues involved in a great many newspaper items that they have simply passed over before; that they are aware of the fields and the crops they drive by, and see now signs of erosion, and estimate the cost of the machinery and the buildings.

At this point it is appropriate to turn to some accounts of what these faculty, from their new sensitivity to the agricultural society they are embedded in, have made happen at their respective campuses. The authors of the next sections were all members of the first summer seminar and, since then, have worked together as coordinators of the Consortium's activities on their respective campuses. Their reports include reflections on the particular shape Consortium work has taken at each college, for though the programs are roughly parallel, they are by no means the same.

COE COLLEGE

Cedar Rapids, Iowa

Duane T. Carr

The Setting

Coe College is situated in a residential section of Cedar Rapids, Iowa, a city of about 115,000 people, in the rolling terrain of eastern Iowa. The four-year, liberal arts College was founded in 1851 by the Reverend Williston Jones of the United Presbyterian Church for 16 young men preparing for the ministry. It was established as a permanent institution of higher learning in 1853. Today it serves more than 1,300 full- and part-time students annually, granting the degrees of bachelor of arts, music, and science in nursing.

One of Coe College's primary missions is to stimulate and encourage students to think critically and self-critically. In addition to providing traditional on-campus programs which help students acquire such skills, the College enables students to gain experience in the larger society. This is accomplished through off-campus programs for observing and studying in urban centers of government and the arts in this country and abroad, and for working in industry, banking, public education, social services, health services, government and politics, and in a great range of other fields. Most recently, the College expanded its learning opportunities to include the Consortium's Agriculture and World Hunger program. While the effort is primarily confined to on-campus activities, it gives students *and* faculty a chance to apply their substantive knowledge to the field of agriculture.

Duane T. Carr is associate professor of chemistry at Coe College, Cedar Rapids, IA.

Program Plan

Coe College's plan for participating in the Consortium's Agriculture and World Hunger program included five key objectives. First, it would encourage as many faculty members as possible to attend the Consortium's summer seminars. From these experiences it was hoped that participants would learn how to introduce agriculturally related topics into regular courses at the College and that they would get ideas for new courses bearing on agriculture. The new courses would be taught during the January term, a period during which Coe faculty members are encouraged to offer special courses outside the regular curriculum. Second, the program would help faculty members implement necessary curriculum changes. This would include the addition of agriculture into the orientation process. Third, Coe planned to integrate agricultural topics into a program of convocations. Speakers from the field would be invited to talk to the public and to student groups regarding important and timely agriculturally related issues. Fourth, the College would introduce independent study projects with agriculture themes for students. These projects would be directed by the faculty. Finally, Coe would develop a collection of books and journals on agriculture.

Program Organization

The Consortium project was and continues to be headed by professor Harland Nelson of Luther College. On the Coe campus, a committee comprised of Coe faculty members who attended the Consortium's summer seminar were responsible for setting up and carrying out the local program, while keeping in contact with professor Nelson.

Each year the committee presented a program for all of Coe's faculty. At these sessions the committee described the Agriculture and World Hunger program and discussed information obtained from the summer seminars. The committee also set up college-community workshops. In addition, it worked with a convocation committee to plan a convocation series on topics related to agriculture. The convocation series usually involved a program held on Monday evenings for the entire community and a regular convocation program conducted on Tuesday mornings for students and faculty.

Process and Product

The most notable result of the project was the faculty interest it generated. At first, the dean of the College was able to find only two faculty members who would participate in the program, largely because the notification of the summer seminar came out rather late. (Many people already had commitments for the summer.)

That fall the two faculty members who attended the seminar set up a program for the entire Coe faculty. A film, "The Stephens of Iowa," was shown. This film is one of a series entitled "Six Families," which depicts the lives and problems of typical families in different areas of the country. The Stephens are an Iowa farm family who deal with many of the concerns faced by farmers across the country. The film was discussed by faculty members and the relation of agricultural concerns to Coe's liberal arts curriculum was pointed out. Additionally, the two faculty members talked about their summer experience and many people became interested in the project. Four people were recruited for the second summer seminar and interest increased each subsequent year.

Individuals attending the summer programs came from the fields of biology, chemistry, physics, economics, psychology, sociology, finance, nursing, physical education, and religion. This indicated a wide range of interest in the program.

Agriculturally related topics were integrated into several existing courses by the faculty members who had participated in the summer seminar. For example, an economics instructor added a segment on U.S. agriculture to his introductory economics course, and is in the process of introducing an even larger agricultural segment in "Current Economic Problems." In the course "Economic Development of the Third World," global food and population problems are now being discussed in detail. Similarly, the instructor of "Social Problems" is merging discussions of rural and urban social structures in his class. A teacher of "Introduction to Modern Culture" is applying his new familiarity with contemporary farm issues by showing the relevance of Missouri farmer Wayne Crites' problem with a bankrupt grain elevator to class discussions of Henry David Thoreau. In addition, he is pointing out changes in agriculture which support changes in culture. Students in a nursing course dealing with health care systems now consider the particular problems of health on the farm; this course also offers many possibilities for farm-linked independent study projects. In a basic chemistry course, chemical fertilizers and their relation to energy resources are discussed. And a course in "Environmental Studies" is exploring the effects of soil loss, a particularly large environmental problem for Iowa, as well as questions on the use of chemical fertilizers and pesticides.

Two wholly new courses were created as a result of the Consortium program. One is a sociology course. William Flanagan, a sociologist and member of the College's project advisory committee, teaches the senior seminar for sociology majors in alternate years. He set up a course which he calls "Rural Sociology." Professor Flanagan is interested in the small towns of Iowa, and their relationship to surrounding farm communities. The course deals with the changing aspects of rural life and culture in Iowa, and the many outside forces which impinge on it. A part of the course involves visits to a number of farms and farm-related businesses in the area.

Also, Coe College developed a course to be conducted during the winter term, a period in January when students take only one course. In 1983, two members of the advisory committee taught a course which they called "Land and People: The Politics of World Hunger." The course was very successful. Students from Africa, Arab Countries, South America, Southeast Asia, as well as the United States (Coe College has a number of foreign students) enrolled. The sharing of information and attitudes from various parts of the world was an important part of the course. The course will be continued, probably on alternate years.

A particularly effective part of the program was the convocation series. In addition to speaking at convocations, Coe College invited regularly scheduled speakers to meet with classes and to hold less formal discussions with faculty and students over lunch or at informal receptions. Speakers included, for example, Frances Moore Lappe, director of the Institute for Food and Development Policy. Lappe visited the campus in January 1983 in connection with the course on "Agriculture and World Hunger." The Institute, with headquarters in San Francisco, California, is a strong advocate of local control over farming and food policies, believing that a major problem has been the existence of large companies which take away not only local initiative, but also many of the profits in local areas of the world. To contrast this position, Thomas Atwood, executive with Archer Daniels Midland, visited the campus and participated in the convocation series. Archer Daniels Midland is a large multinational company with a corn processing plant in Cedar Rapids, and Mr. Atwood ably expressed the outlook of the company. Both individuals made themselves available for less formal discussions. Students, faculty, and many people from the Cedar Rapids community heard their messages. Reports in student newspapers indicated good understanding of their views of world hunger, and thoughtful consideration of the issues raised by them.

Coe College found it difficult, however, to build significant material on agriculture into the orientation process. Orientation programs, already very crowded, could not accommodate the addition of agricultural topics of meaningful length to the schedule. Instead, farm visits and other informative programs were added to student learning experiences during the year. For example, a small number of students in the spring of 1983 visited a plant geneticist at Grinnell to learn about the development of hybrid corn, and a student faculty contingent visited the Amana colonies to discuss the agricultural enterprise there. Amana was originally a communistic group of small farming communities which changed to a capitalistic corporation in 1932. A board oversees the agricultural program of all the colonies, and they use many innovative agricultural practices.

An evolving aspect of Coe's program is the independent study component. With the Kellogg grant, the College has been adding a number of titles dealing with agriculture and its relation to society to its library. It is now in a position to carry out student study projects, particularly in the areas of rural sociology and in farm economics.

Lessons Learned

A major problem with the Consortium's Agriculture and World Hunger program on the Coe campus was the lack of organization. The original grant did not provide funds for release time from classwork for someone to administer the local program. Such a position would be very useful and would centralize the efforts of the people associated with the project. Had there been such a person, it would have solved another particular problem

— that of publicity. The program reached a number of people from the local community and the Coe campus, but it should reach more members of farming communities around Cedar Rapids. Without someone to work directly on publicity efforts, the additional outreach has not been possible. Faculty members do not have enough time, in addition to the classes they teach, to do the necessary work to bring all parts of the community together.

Despite these problems, the program has been particularly valuable, and will have a continuing influence. A central group of faculty participated in the summer studies. This group brought back many new ideas, several of which have been incorporated into Coe coursework. Coe College can point directly to some new courses, and to new sections in other courses, which deal with agricultural topics.

More difficult to pinpoint, but probably even more valuable, is the increased awareness of the individuals associated with the programs. Because of the program, students and faculty are more cognizant of agricultural matters. Coe College continues to feature agricultural issues in its convocation programs. In the coming year, it hopes to conduct another workshop, perhaps in cooperation with other local groups, on agriculture-related topics. Agriculture has become a part of many courses in diverse parts of the campus. In a small way, agriculture has become a topic of liberal arts.

CORNELL COLLEGE

Mt. Vernon, Iowa

David L. Lyon

The Setting

Cornell College is located in Mount Vernon, in eastern central Iowa on U.S. Highway 30, approximately 15 miles east of Cedar

David L. Lyon is professor of biology at Cornell College, Mt. Vernon, IA.

Rapids and 300 miles west of Chicago. The College is a privately-supported, residential, coeducational, liberal arts college known for more than a century and a quarter for its academic excellence. It offers four baccalaureate degree programs: bachelor of arts, music, philosophy, and special studies.

Cornell possesses an environment that was uniquely conducive to the establishment of the Consortium's Agriculture and World Hunger program. Close interaction among faculty members and between faculty and students; a low student faculty ratio; and a campus that represents a microcosm of society and is located near rich farmland, all combined to provide an excellent training ground for students as they learned about the significance of agriculture to the world.

Program Plan

Upon deciding to participate in the Consortium's Agriculture and World Hunger program, Cornell College decided to focus its activities on incorporating knowledge about agriculture into *existing* courses. (Since Cornell has no "interim" or "January" term, it was unable to design and offer special courses outside the regular curriculum.)

Cornell approached this objective cautiously. Past experiences with grants designed to restructure the institution's curriculum around certain goals had been bitter; in most cases as soon as external funding ended so did the new courses. Fearing that the same might happen again, the College pledged to obtain the support of its faculty. It reasoned that the faculty would be most apt to implement lasting curricular changes if they were knowledgeable and interested in the subject.

Fortunately, Cornell's faculty already contained a latent coterie of individuals with backgrounds, experiences, or interests in agriculture. Cornell hoped that this preexisting interest in agriculture would blossom through the provision of workshops on agricultural topics of local interest. Plans were immediately set in motion to hold at least one faculty workshop yearly during the life of the project. Community symposiums on agricultural issues would be conducted as well.

Program Organization

Initially, program organization was loose. Since no one was appointed coordinator, a committee system was used to mutually agree on duties as the occasion demanded. This arrangement soon proved unsatisfactory, however. When the number of summer seminar participants grew the second year, the need became evident for an official campus coordinator.

In September 1982, a coordinator was named. He was given responsibility for calling meetings and maintaining liaison with the Consortium at Luther College. The committee continued to handle arrangements for campus talks, meals, social events, and transportation. This division of labor worked well for all. Program organization was greatly facilitated by the appointment of faculty members to the summer seminars. This meant that over the project's lifetime approximately 14 percent (9 of 66) of the Cornell faculty had an opportunity to be involved in project activities. All nine were expected to become involved in some phase of planning for workshops and symposiums.

Many summer participants eventually participated in the workshops and symposiums, introducing participants, leading discussion groups, and acting as respondents to speakers. Other faculty members also helped out in similar capacities.

During the first two years, combining good sense and serendipity, the College entered into a symbiotic relationship with a local Chapter of the League of Women Voters. This happened because the League was engaged in a study of U.S. and state soil conservation policies in the fall of 1982. Its involvement dovetailed nicely with Cornell's interests so they combined forces; the College contingent used Kellogg moneys to sponsor symposiums and the League provided publicity services. The League's most successful form of publicity turned out to be personal invitations to faculty leaders, friends, and acquaintances. Articles announcing upcoming symposiums in Mount Vernon, Cedar Rapids, and Iowa City newspapers generally attracted few out-of-towners, although the appearance of former Secretary of Agriculture Bob Bergland in the 1983 spring symposium was an exception.

Process and Product

Faculty Workshops

The first faculty workshop in December 1981 was organized around the theme "Resource Conservation on the Iowa Farm." Four panel members offered their views on local energy and soil conservation matters. Don Freeman, a county agent, described what soil erosion is and what techniques can be used to minimize it. Dennis Uthof, head of the Mount Vernon branch of Hertz Farm Management, Inc., spoke of ways to minimize energy consumption. Keith Kirkpatrick, a local farmer with experience in minimum tillage, discussed some practical problems associated with minimum or no-till agriculture; and Duane Sand, formerly of the Soil Conservation Service but now with the Iowa Heritage Foundation (an Iowa-based foundation concerned with nature and resource conservation and historical preservation), talked about the moral imperatives which he believes should guide soil conservation and land preservation practices. About 15 faculty and 15 invited guests from the student body and community attended. The workshop was judged to be an unqualified success, largely because *locally* respected panelists dealt with *local* agricultural problems.

In 1982, two faculty workshops were held. In September, Dr. Edwinn Wellhausen, until recently head of the Rockefeller Foundation's maize improvement breeding program in Mexico, discussed with a group of 26 faculty and guests and six students the short- and long-term prospects for food production in the Third World. The gist of his argument was that the improvement of maize varieties for high tech farming has been eagerly used by large landowners, and hence annual production has increased steadily. Since small peasant farmers cannot use this technology, new varieties and strategies must be developed to help ease them out of poverty.

In December, ex-Senator Dick Clark of Iowa spoke to 35 individuals (31 faculty, 4 students, two of whom were African) about U.S. international agricultural policy and its effects on African agriculture. He concluded that although U.S. policy has helped to stifle local agricultural expertise, in some cases, many African leaders do not regard indigenous agriculture as especially important as long as food can be imported for urban populations, the source of their political power.

Community Symposiums

In April 1982, the first community symposium featured Lauren Soth, former farm columnist and farm editor for the Des Moines *Register.* He spoke about "The Effect of U.S. Export Policy on Iowa Agriculture." One of his main concerns was the effect of soil erosion on sustained intensive use of cropland for corn and soybeans targeted for export. He questioned whether Iowans are literally selling the future productivity of their soils down the river. The four panelists who participated in the first faculty workshop responded and a fruitful discussion followed. Over 50 people attended, including many League of Women Voter members and their guests. Following the discussion, faculty members who had participated in the Consortium's summer seminars led small group discussions on "World Hunger and Population Growth," "Resource Conservation on the Iowa Farm," and "Appropriate Technologies for the Iowa Farm."

Two community symposiums were held in 1982-83. In an address on "Food Production in the Tropics" Dr. Edwinn Wellhausen, special staff member of the Rockefeller Foundation, assessed the prospects for feeding the growing populations of Third World tropical countries. With the exception of Africa and a few countries in South America and Asia, he concluded that food production will match population growth in the short term, but that population has to be stabilized in the long run if serious economic and political problems are to be avoided. About 200 faculty, students, and townspeople attended the symposium.

In March 1983, Bob Bergland, consultant, Farmlands Eaton, spoke to a group of approximately 75 faculty, students, farmers, and townspeople about "American Agriculture: A Time to Choose." He reiterated many of the points made in the book of the same name published by the U.S. Department of Agriculture while he was Secretary of Agriculture in the Carter Administration. His talk, as might be expected, was wide ranging and multifaceted; among his main theses were these points:

the U.S. Department of Agriculture needs to be more concerned with long-term policy formation than with immediate economic circumstances and pressures;

the family farm and rural way of life is worth preserving because it encourages desirable values and because it is cost effective compared to large-scale farming operations; and the high cost of land prevents young people who want to begin farming from buying farmland; one of its causes — land speculation — could be minimized by corrected legislation.

An unofficial audience poll immediately following the talk showed his presentation was well received. Mr. Bergland also had lunch with about 25 faculty members and held a question and answer session for political science, history, and economics classes.

Coursework

The Kellogg faculty workshops and community symposiums generated some rather interesting alterations in some courses. Following are a few examples of how faculty members integrated agricultural concerns into their existing coursework.

David Lyon (Biology) partially reorganized two courses to reflect the importance and influence of agriculture on organisms. (He plans on teaching a third course which will serve as a vehicle to emphasize agriculturally related themes from time to time.) In an ecology course, life histories and ecological strategies of wild plants are compared to those of crop and pasture plants. This comparison shows that crop plants share many characteristics of wild plants commonly called "weeds," and that their similarities provide fresh insights for managing cropland systems more effectively. In an ornithology course, which traditionally included a lecture or two about the effect of human activities on bird populations, he deals with the positive and negative effects of agriculture on birds in Iowa, including suggestions for ameliorating some negative effects.

Paul Christiansen (Biology), a plant ecologist, has been responsible at Cornell for courses in plant morphology, plant taxonomy, and plant physiology. He found it difficult to introduce agricultural topics into these rather standardized courses, with the exception of plant physiology. In the latter course, he uses an occasional laboratory experiment to emphasize specific physiological mechanisms that are important to agriculture. Additionally, he features agricultural examples in lectures to illustrate general ecological principles.

Douglas Hanson (Art) incorporated information related to agriculture into three courses. In a photography course, students are required to choose a theme around which to do a photo interpretive study. Professor Hanson has coaxed several students to do their projects on agriculture and farming. In Ceramics I and II, which are taught in Mexico, he familiarizes students with Mexican peasant agriculture through the pottery farmers manufacture and use for agricultural purposes. And in an African art course, he discusses and compares the agriculturally related art of tribal groups. (Many of the tribes' art objects are agricultural implements or symbolically refer to some agricultural phenomenon.) The aesthetic nature and relevance of objects are then discussed in relation to agricultural functions.

Hardie Park (Economics) taught three courses directly related to agriculture: General Economics, Economics Development, and International Economics. Professor Park's experience at the Consortium's summer seminar convinced him that American agriculture is increasingly dependent on crop exports, especially soybeans and corn. Consequently the professor designed his beginning economics coursework to help students understand the implications of this fact. He also expanded course materials to include discussions on the role of large corporations in the rise of commercial farming. While teaching International Economics in 1983-84 he gave special emphasis to the importance of international grain trade, to growing food deficits in Third World countries (particularly Africa), and to the poignant relevance of oil economics to food deficits. In 1984-85 the course's main theme was that agricultural development is a prerequisite for general economic development unless there are other special resources or commodities that can be sold internationally, e.g., minerals or manufactured goods.

Eugene Hinman (Geology) used knowledge gained from the Consortium's summer seminar in two courses: Earth Science and Historical Geology. In Earth Science, Professor Hinman strengthened treatment of the origin and evolution of soil, soil as a resource, and soil conservation. In Historical Geology he integrated new material gleaned from the summer seminar on the origin and evolution of soils.

Edward Hill (Mathematics). It is not easy for a mathematician to integrate agricultural subjects in a math class! In several math courses such as Calculus, however, Professor Hill has used agriculturally related examples (e.g., population growth and world food growth) to demonstrate various mathematic functions.

Lessons Learned

It is difficult to assess accurately the impact of the program on various constituencies. Several faculty members and townspeople have praised the workshops and symposiums and have asked to be kept on the "guest list" for all future events. From these statements, program leaders have concluded that workshops and symposiums have served their intended purpose of raising agricultural awareness and of increasing and broadening agricultural knowledge among faculty and townspeople.

Assessment is more difficult for the primary target group: students. It is impossible to tell how the curricular changes are affecting students without careful analysis. While Cornell plans to initiate an indepth study at the end of the program, it currently has only anecdotal evidence by which to assess the impact of the program on its intended audience.

Cornell's Agriculture and World Hunger program appears to have two limiting factors: (1) the paucity of courses in the liberal arts where agriculture is the primary concern, and (2) the relatively few disciplines represented in the program. The first difficulty is insurmountable. Liberal arts colleges are not land-grant institutions and their faculties generally will not approve courses with primary agricultural biases unless they fit established departmental structures. Thus, if a sociology professor has a professional interest in rural sociology, that individual may be permitted to introduce rural sociology in departmental offerings, but it is unlikely that many such courses will become part of the regular curriculum. It may be that a smattering of agriculture in several classes, supplemented by a cadre of outside speakers on agricultural topics, is the most efficient way of handling the matter, and the most that can be expected at an institution such as Cornell.

The second difficulty appears to be more manageable. The program hopes to involve an additional 10 to 12 faculty members in summer seminars and faculty workshops. Several individuals have voiced an interest in being included. They come from departments other than those now represented. Their involvement in the program would increase the probability that Cornell students would encounter agriculture in sociology, business education, French, health and physical education, music, political science, philosophy, and religion. Unfortunately, the summer seminars often compete with other professional activities, making it necessary for many faculty members to decline invitations to participate. Extending the summer seminar program from three years to four or five years might enable more faculty members to attend the sessions.

What will be sustained after Kellogg support terminates? Much of what is being done, will continue. All faculty members who have been involved in the effort to date seem committed to add or restructure courses to accommodate agricultural concerns. Further, Cornell's recent success with workshops and symposiums on agriculture is likely to encourage more lecturers on agricultural subjects under the sponsorship of traditional campus funding sources. As a result, students may yet gain insight into the importance agriculture plays in society today.

GRINNELL COLLEGE

Grinnell, Iowa

Wayne Moyer

The Setting

Grinnell College, a four-year liberal arts college enrolling 1200 students, was founded at Davenport, Iowa, in 1846 (the same year Iowa became a state) by a small group of Congregational ministers, the Iowa Band. The College was moved to Grinnell in 1859. It was known as Iowa College until 1900 when it assumed the name of the town founder, J. B. Grinnell, who came to Iowa in 1854 after Horace Greeley told him to "Go West, young man, go West."

Of the four colleges in the Consortium on Agriculture and World Hunger, Grinnell probably has the weakest tie to contemporary U.S. agriculture. Our student body is largely suburban

Wayne Moyer is associate professor of political science at Grinnell College, Grinnell, IA.

with very few students coming directly from farming backgrounds. In fact, only about 12 percent of the student population comes from Iowa and, as a result, we cannot even count on the rudimentary knowledge gained from growing up in this incredibly productive farming region. Before the Kellogg grant, our curriculum — with its heavy emphasis on the traditional liberal arts — did not do a great deal to close this knowledge gap. Students in biology courses gained an understanding of seed genetics and plant physiology, and concern for soil conservation, pesticide and chemical use was part and parcel of the College's environmental studies interdisciplinary concentration. Students who studied Iowa history gained a general understanding of farming in this state. But, there was not much else.

Outside the curriculum, food and agricultural issues were not completely ignored by the College. Grinnell has a long tradition of preparing students for domestic and international public service. Hence, current public policy issues have been intensely debated on campus, often with outside speakers. When food issues have risen to the top of the national policy agenda, they have been discussed rather extensively at Grinnell. Indeed, in 1975 the College sponsored a major food conference, "Food, Famine, and Foreign Policy," in response to the world food crisis of the early 1970s. The College's awareness and willingness to address such issues head-on made it an excellent site for the Consortium's Agriculture and World Hunger program.

The Program Plan

In the late 1970s, discussion began at Grinnell on ways the College could better prepare students to understand future agricultural policy choices. It was the faculty's belief that agricultural questions would be of great salience in the 1980s and 1990s. Learning of the Kellogg Foundation's interest in an agriculture-in-the-liberal arts program, the College's faculty members seized the opportunity to galvanize these discussions by joining the Consortium in its grant proposal submitted to the Kellogg Foundation.

When the College was told that the Consortium had been awarded a grant from Kellogg, the dean of the faculty immediately created a local steering committee to guide Grinnell's effort.

The committee consisted of a biologist with a strong interest in environmental questions, an economist with an interest in land use and soil conservation, a political scientist (chairman) interested in international food policy who had just finished a sabbatical at Stanford's Food Research Institute, and a French professor who had long felt that agriculture should be a central concern of the liberal arts College.

The group had no strong preconceptions about what Grinnell should do. We decided that one of the most feasible and potentially productive strategies to maximize the agricultural awareness of students was to increase the number of speakers coming to campus to talk about food-related topics. (The steering committee considered combining Kellogg funds with others from the College's new Rosenfield Program on Public Affairs, International Relations, and Human Rights to finance the events.) We also discussed how the College might address agricultural issues in the context of the other disciplines. For instance, Grinnell might focus on the problems of Soviet agriculture in our Russian and East European studies program. The steering committee decided, however, to leave curriculum questions to individual faculty members. Instead, we defined our role as one of developing faculty interest, then supporting individual faculty members as each innovated in ways which seemed compatible with the proposal.

Process and Products

Grinnell was fortunate that all four members of the steering committee were able to attend the first summer seminar of the Colloquium at Luther College in Decorah. All of us found this a valuable experience, providing a good basis for the first campus activity — the Grinnell faculty workshop held in October 1981. The workshop was kicked off with a Friday evening dinner that was attended by 25 of the College's 100 faculty members. Following the dinner, general discussions of the Kellogg program and of various aspects of the world food problem took place. Saturday was devoted to an all-day field trip, first to the Cargill experimental seed plot and then to the Amana farm. This workshop succeeded in increasing faculty interest and helped to develop a sense of camaraderie among interested professors. Prior to this time, we had only limited awareness of each other's concerns.

The second activity was a minicourse on "U.S. Agriculture and World Hunger" held during October 1981. One of the provisions of the Kellogg grant called for intensive one-month courses. These were not feasible at Grinnell, which has no interim session, so the steering committee decided to hold a four-day intensive course over fall break. During the course, mornings were spent in the classroom discussing such topics as "The Changing Structure of U.S. Agriculture," "The Politics of Food in the U.S.," and "Overcoming World Hunger: the Challenge Ahead." Afternoons were spent visiting local farms, the local Golden Sun Feed Plant, and the Cargill experimental seed plot.

Forty-four students expressed an interest in this minicourse; 32 actually gave up their vacation to participate. The experience was highly worthwhile in stimulating student interest early in the project; and it came during the harvest, which is an excellent time to observe farm operations. However, the minicourse subverted to some extent the primary purpose of the break — to provide a respite for students and faculty from the normal intensive classroom routine.

Grinnell's lecture program began in the spring of 1982 with a February talk, "The New Deal for American Agriculture," by Richard Kirkendall, Henry Wallace professor of history at Iowa State University. This lecture was given in conjunction with a Rosenfield program symposium on the centennial of the birth of President Franklin D. Roosevelt. That same month, Professor Vernon Ruttan of the University of Minnesota gave an all-college convocation on how the world feeds itself. The event was attended by about 300 people from the College and the surrounding community. Ruttan also gave a lecture on induced technical change. Finally, in an April community symposium, a joint discussion was held between Robbin Johnson, assistant vice president of Cargill for Public Affairs, and former Iowa U.S. Senator Dick Clark. Their topic was the hunger problem in Africa. As part of the symposium Johnson also gave a public lecture on "Iowa and the World Grain Economy." About 200 students and 100 townspeople attended.

The 1982 fall semester got off to a fast start with a three-day conference in September on Soviet-American agricultural relations. This conference was keynoted by Victor Lishchenko, head of the Food and Agriculture Department of the Soviet Institute of the USA and Canada, who talked on "Modern Problems in Soviet

Agriculture." Other speakers included Professor D. Gale Johnson of the University of Chicago, who lectured on "The Soviet Union and World Grain Economy," and Dr. Leo V. Mayer, associate administrator of USDA's Foreign Agricultural Service, who discussed "U.S. Policy on the Soviet-American Grain Trade." There were also panels on "Contrasting Iowa and Soviet Perspectives" and on "The Prospects for the Future." These sessions were well attended with more than 600 from the College and community represented.

In addition to holding the conference, Grinnell introduced a new four-credit course on "Problems and Politics of Food and Agriculture" in 1982. The course included units on the development of American agriculture, food policy issues and the policy-making process, and agriculture in developed and developing countries. Twenty students enrolled in this course, about equally divided among those majoring in the sciences, humanities, and the social studies. Each student had the responsibility of an independent research project. Some of the best of these were built around farm visits and interviews with local farmers and agribusiness managers.

Other course offerings were developed around food related issues in the spring of 1983. The senior seminar of the College's environmental studies interdisciplinary concentration focused on farming. Participants wrote papers on farming in the United States and Third World countries. Group independent study was offered on current economic issues in U.S. agriculture by the Economics Department. And a unit of the political science seminar on "The Politics of Land and Sea Resources" centered on world food problems in the 1980s.

For the spring 1983 symposium, Grinnell sponsored what amounted to a debate between Professor Earl Heady of Iowa State University, speaking for the agricultural establishment, and Wendell Berry, speaking for the counterculture critics. Heady discussed the reasons why the continuing trend toward big farms makes good economic sense, while Berry lamented how this trend destroys important rural values and endangers the long-term productivity of the land. This well-attended symposium generated heated discussions. The audience was provided a good sense of the trade-offs between farm income and preservation of traditional rural life that are made daily.

Other spring speakers were Iowa banker John Chrystal, who

gave his personal impressions of farming in the U.S.S.R. as a follow-up to our fall conference, and Harold P. Lee, who spoke on Roswell Garst, "An Extraordinary Iowa Farmer." The planners of the College's "Conference on Revolution, Reaction and Reform in Central America," sponsored jointly by the Rosenfield program and the Iowa Humanities Board, included agriculture as a focus with a panel on agricultural reform and rural development.

Lessons Learned

The most striking success of the Kellogg program has been in bringing together the faculty members of the participating institutions with their own colleagues and with those from the other institutions both in the summer seminars at Luther and in events on the individual campuses. All of us have become more sensitized to current agricultural issues and there has been a great deal of information sharing. At Grinnell, the Kellogg consortium has provided a very nice mechanism for promoting faculty awareness of the problems of contemporary agriculture and has been the motivating force for increasing the number of things the College does related to food and agriculture. The summer seminars were seen by Grinnell faculty as highly valuable, and we could have generated more volunteers had slots been available. When the program started, the strongly interested group consisted of only four faculty members with probably an equal number having somewhat more peripheral interest. The hard core now includes all the summer seminar participants, and the peripheral group has expanded to about 25. There clearly was an impact on the curriculum, though the final shape of that impact is not yet clear.

Students also were positively affected by the program. The College estimates that, as a result of the effort, about half of the student body was sensitized to agricultural questions. Lectures and symposiums probably were the most effective means of coverage, while course innovations, minicourses and independent projects promoted depth of understanding. By continuing the efforts begun by the Consortium, we think we can do much more to increase student sophistication at Grinnell. The strategy of linking Agriculture and World Hunger activities to other ongoing curricular concerns appears to work well.

Another somewhat unanticipated benefit of the Kellogg program was the inclusion of a whole new section of the Grinnell community in College activities. A significant number of farmers and agribusiness people attended lectures and symposiums and participated in the discussions. College participants learned at least as much from them as they did from the College. Moreover, there is little doubt that students' respect for farmers and their problems greatly increased due to program activities. In addition, faculty and students forged valuable personal ties with farmers and agribusiness leaders. This cannot help but increase their understanding of U.S. agriculture.

As with all the Consortium programs, freshman orientation was a weak point at Grinnell. While the College offered a farm tour to all incoming freshmen, only 50 out of 360 took advantage each year. If anything significant is going to be done, the farm tour has to be taken out of new student orientation days.

While it may be too soon for a final assessment, most curricular innovations have come from a small number of faculty members. The incentives provided by the grant do not appear strong enough in this respect. More must be done in motivating curricular changes through faculty release time and summer course development incentives.

LUTHER COLLEGE

Decorah, Iowa

Harland S. Nelson

The Setting

Decorah, Iowa, the home of Luther College, is a community of about 8,000, the county seat of Winneshiek County, and the most important trading center in this largely agricultural northeast corner of the state. The College was moved here in 1862, having been founded a year earlier in a rural location near LaCrosse, Wisconsin, as a college of the Norwegian Evangelical Lutheran Church in America. The connection to the church has been continuous, and Luther College today is affiliated with the American Lutheran Church, the successor of the founding church body. Luther is a four-year liberal arts college; it awards a single degree, the bachelor of arts, to all its graduates. Begun as a college for men, Luther became coeducational in 1936; the current enrollment is about 2,100.

The Program Plan

Besides directing the Consortium, I was my own campus coordinator. This combining of roles was urged by my Luther colleagues at the first summer seminar (these individuals were on call as an advisory committee, as were the members of the second and third seminars in subsequent years). As coordinator I picked the Luther faculty members who were to be part of each summer seminar, and I planned each year's campus program. Fortunately, I did not have to work hard to drum up interest; a substantial number of the faculty at Luther either grew up on a farm (as I did), or had near relatives who farm. A few lived on farms near Decorah, and were personally involved in actual farming operations to some degree. Thus, the interest in the Consortium was broadly distributed through the faculty, and each year I had to disappoint several people who wanted to be part of the summer seminar and of the activities following from that.

Planning the program, I relied on the structure of events and activities envisioned in the project as approved by the Kellogg Foundation. Apart from the January term course, I left curricular revisions to develop from the summer seminar, for the same reasons David Lyon gave in his report on the Cornell program. The annual fall faculty workshops were jointly conceived and planned by me and my successive advisory committees. Most of my time as Luther's coordinator, however, went to the public symposium, probably because the work of planning the summer seminars led me to think about topics of general concern, and to find out who could teach the most about those topics.

Process and Product

Faculty Workshops

For the first workshop we figured on making as wide an impression as we could; accordingly, we baited the occasion with a free dinner for faculty participants and spouses. The workshop itself was a two-hour panel discussion open to the whole campus population. The three summer seminarians gave brief presentations on highlights of the seminar, and in the course of the general discussion which followed, they were very persuasive examples of how effective the seminar was at providing information and generating interest and concern.

That workshop was the most heavily attended of the three, probably because the project was new and the focus we announced for the workshop promised to yield a clear overview. About 70 faculty members and their spouses attended the dinner, and approximately 175 people from the whole campus community were present for the panel discussion. This level of attendance was considered remarkable for an event held the evening before the start of the midsemester break. The second and third workshops began with brief field trips, one to a family dairy farm at milking time, the other to a farm where terracing — a farming practice which, through the growing of crops on various levels, maximizes the use of water and minimizes soil erosion problems — is extensively practiced. Following the field trip we had a meal together, and a discussion afterwards; the farmers and their families were our guests for the meal and resource people for the discussion. We also had a local banker as our guest and resource person at the third workshop, so the discussion ranged well beyond terracing into the economics of the family farm.

Students were invited to take part in these workshops, too, and a handful — 8 or 10 — did each time. As for faculty, between 20 and 30 took part in each; total attendance at all three workshops amounted to well over half the faculty (meaning that 40 percent or so, discounting repeaters, have taken part to date in at least one workshop). I do not discount the free meal as a draw, but it is clear that interest in the subject matter was genuine, and opinion of the workshops' value was very favorable.

The January Term Course

We have offered an interdisciplinary course, "Farming, Food, and the Future," each year, taught by the cadre from the seminar of the preceding summer. The course content was determined by the faculty involved and was varied each year; however, all three offerings have featured field trips and consultants from the local area, as well as the usual array of instructional tools: required texts, films, journal-keeping, and individual projects. One team required the students to take the Des Moines *Register* for the month and to survey it daily — an effective way to make the point that, in Iowa, farming is important news.

Course enrollment was about 35 students the first year, half that number the second (another farm-centered course had a similar enrollment at that time), and 75 the third. There is a lesson in that leap which I will discuss later.

The Symposiums

We held four symposiums: spring and fall 1982, spring 1983, and spring 1984 (deferred for calendar reasons from fall 1983). All were open to the general public; all followed a format of presentations by guest speakers, with a response by a panel of local people, and audience participation after that. For the first one, "Controlling Soil Erosion: What Works Best? Who Pays for It? (spring 1982), the presenters were Clayton Wangsness, a local farmer thoroughly committed to soil-conserving methods, and Lauren Soth, long-time agriculture columnist for the *Register* and *Tribune Syndicate*. I invested most of my budget in advertising the event in weekly newspapers in northeast Iowa, hoping to draw significant attendance by farmers. As I remember, the farmers in the audience cost about $50 apiece in advertising to get them there. Another lesson. I continued to advertise later symposiums, but only in the local newspaper and with considerably contracted expectations.

However, attendance did grow significantly from one symposium to the next. "Will Exports Bring Back Farm Profits?" (fall 1982) featured Philip Raup, professor of agricultural and applied economics at the University of Minnesota; Don Muhm, Des Moines *Register* farm editor; and Robert Lounsberry, Iowa secretary of agriculture. It drew about 90 people — students, faculty, townspeople, and a few farmers. "Food Production in the Developing Countries" (spring 1983), with papers by Charlotte Roderuck, director of the World Food Institute at Iowa State University; J. W. Pendleton, professor of agronomy at the University of Wisconsin; and Norman Borlaug, Nobel Peace Prize winner of "green revolution" fame; had an audience of about 350 people. The leap in this case was certainly due to the presence of Dr. Borlaug. But the following spring "Water Resources and Farming: Changing Perspectives" drew about 125 people to hear presentations by Stephen Ballou, director of the Iowa Department of Water, Air, and Waste Management; and Sandra Gardebring, director of the Minnesota Pollution Control Agency. All the symposiums were gratifyingly received, with the two on exports and water resources bringing the most favorable comment.

Student Orientation

Luther was no more successful in developing a student orientation component than any of the other colleges in the Consortium. We did take a few students along on the faculty workshops, as I mentioned, but we developed nothing along the lines envisioned in the proposal. (See the discussion of this under "Summing Up the Consortium.")

Lessons Learned

As noted earlier, enrollment in the January term course doubled in the third year. The explanation is that the course, meanwhile, was approved to meet a general college requirement. The lesson is clear, and consistent with the whole underlying philosophy of the Consortium: the way to effectively introduce agriculture and food production to students is to integrate the topic into the regular liberal arts course work, rather than to rely solely on providing elective options.

When to hold community symposiums, so as to attract the most people, was an important question. Three of the four symposiums were scheduled for Saturday mornings; the one featuring Dr. Borlaug had to be scheduled on a Thursday afternoon to fit in with his commitments at Iowa State University and at the Iowa Academy of Science (held that week at Luther). The idea was to pick a time which would conflict least with students' classes; which faculty, farmers, and townspeople might find convenient; and in which guest lecturers could take part with minimal disruption of their own schedules. Saturday morning seemed like the best compromise, and it still seems like it, after the fact.

If I were to do it all again I would worry less about finding the right time for farmers to attend. Weather is unpredictable, and it often rules farmers' schedules. The same is true of competing events. The symposium on soil erosion, scheduled three months ahead, turned out to be in competition with a big farm auction that offered farmers the prospect of attractive bargains in nearly new machinery. There also is uncertainty among farmers as to whether anything useful to them can come out of a liberal arts college. This skepticism is being dispelled by our program, but it takes time. I will schedule events from now on with my eye on the campus population, and rely on the topic to draw farmers.

SUMMING UP THE CONSORTIUM

Harland S. Nelson

The effects of an ongoing and varied program like this, with different kinds of student contact and different degrees of involvement, cannot be neatly summed up. The outcomes can only be sampled by dipping out a few statistics from time to time. In February 1983 I took such a reading of the year in progress (1982-83), trying to pin numbers to the various sorts of activity going on at the member colleges.

At Coe College, student attendance at public events had totaled about 160; approximately 15 students went on a field trip in September to the Cargill demonstration plot near Grinnell; and the January term course, "Land and People: The Politics of World Hunger," enrolled 16. Events were scheduled for February and March, and a field trip to the Amana colony farms was being planned for the spring.

At Cornell College, about 200 students, faculty, and townspeople — probably half of them students — attended a September convocation by Edwinn Wellhausen on "Food Production in the Tropics." Fall semester enrollment totaled around 180 in courses (art, earth science, ecology, economics) with agricultural content — owing to faculty participation in the summer seminars — ranging from occasional infusion to specific units comprising 10 percent or more of the course.

At Grinnell, student attendance totaled about 600 at the several sessions of the Conference on U.S.-Soviet Agricultural Relations in September. Fifty students took part in a farm tour; 20 took the fall semester course, "Problems and Politics of Food and Agriculture"; and so did some independent studies. Students were then planning a February debate between Wendell Berry (a representative of the agricounterculture, a movement reacting against commercial agriculture which relies on the use of chemicals, herbicides, pesticides, and large equipment in farming), and Earl Heady (a representative of the agricultural "establishment") which promised to draw well.

At Luther, 10 students took part in a fall faculty workshop as guests on a farm tour. Additionally, 10 students attended an Oxfam Community Seminar on Hunger in November on $25 scholarships provided by the Consortium (seed money, it was hoped, for student-led world hunger activity), and 70 attended a public symposium in November ("Will Exports Bring Back Farm Profits?"). Student enrollment in courses totaled 80 in the fall semester course, "Bread, Peace, and Justice" (with a hunger unit drawing on the previous summer's seminar); 17 in the January term course, "Farming Food, and the Future," taught by two Consortium faculty; and 14 in the January term course, "Farming in a Small Way." During the spring, a course in agricultural economics enrolled about 16 (double the usual handful), and about 350 people (students, faculty, townspeople) attended a symposium featuring Dr. Norman Borlaug, of "green revolution" fame.

The Coe Grinnell, and Luther tallies do not include all courses offered during the fall semester which included agricultural elements, so this count is not exhaustive.

The limited data available indicated that the four colleges have been making progress in involving students in the Consortium's Agriculture and World Hunger program. Based on rounded undergraduate population figures for the fall 1982 semester (Coe 1,200; Cornell 830; Grinnell 1,200; Luther 2,000), I estimate that the percentage of students "affected by" or "exposed to" Consortium information was as follows: Coe 16 percent; Cornell 34 percent; Grinnell 35 percent; Luther 10 percent. Two footnotes are in order. (1) Two years ago scarcely any of this was happening. (2) About twice as much was going on in 1982-83 as in 1981-82.

While there is no curricular unit of work at any of the colleges that all students will get, there *are* units of work (and/or significant efforts to focus attention on agriculture and hunger) distributed through enough of the curriculum, and fostered by enough of the faculty, that chances are good that every undergraduate will encounter agricultural issues or concerns. There has also been regular attention to agriculture and food production in public college events.

What kind of afterlife will the Consortium have when Kellogg Foundation funds run out? A reasonably vigorous one, I should think. The kinds of things we have been doing during these three academic years do not take a lot of money. Once the course has been developed, and the topics from agriculture and world food questions are admitted to the pantheon of college-sponsored public events, all that remains to be done is to recruit people who care. Such people were found among the faculties of the four Iowa colleges. Through summer seminars, the Consortium was able to help these individuals focus their interests on agriculture and to give them direction. The seminars helped these people find each other. This last point is important; there is a strong sense of shared enterprise among the three dozen people who have been running the Consortium schedule. It matters to each of us to know there are people in other departments of one's own college who, despite their academic differences, are willing to carry out the program. It matters, too, to know that there are people at three other colleges who are doing the same activities, people to consult and plan with, cooperate with, and perhaps compete with a little. There seems to me to be both structure and spirit, then, for keeping things going.

Some things, though, have not worked out. The proposal envisioned regular offerings of short courses on selected topics at all four colleges. Our collegial calendars have not accommodated these well. Nor have the colleges managed to, as the original proposal states, "design a special emphasis or part of their orientation for new students" that would ensure some kind of contact with local agriculture for every incoming student. (The Grinnell farm tour mentioned by Wayne Moyer is much older than the Consortium.) I am not ready to blame anyone for this; orientation schedules at all the colleges are jammed. Further, serious organizational and logistical problems existed in the proposal. The proposal suggested that the orientation include "a visit to the local agribusiness and a visit to an operating farm in sufficiently small groups to allow dialogue with the farm operator and his family." Some of the larger colleges in the Consortium, such as Luther, would require 40 to 50 such groups. This would mean a heavier investment of time by cooperating local people than is reasonable to expect, and a disproportionate investment of college staff time in planning and implementation.

The colleges also have not been successful in promoting much independent study. Grinnell had a few independent study students in 1982-83; I supervised one in 1981-82; I know of no others. I can see one reason for this. I have not, as Luther's coordinator, done much to stimulate student interest in this area. Neither have I done much, for that matter, to help student affairs people work out some sort of orientation. Nor have I, as director, done the reading I should have, nor have I systematically kept my coordinators on the other campuses informed. Finally, I have not planned the cooperative campus activities that we had originally envisioned from time to time.

I mention these shortcomings as a way of introducing a suggestion for anyone interested in following the Consortium model. Build in enough release time for the director and the coordinators. Two-thirds of my time went to the Consortium the first year, and one-third went to it the second and third years; coordinators have carried their responsibility on top of their regular teaching loads. Ideally, coordinators should have the appropriate amount of release time for carrying out the program responsibilities. A load allowance of two-thirds for the director is probably adequate for the first year (it certainly will not tempt her or him to sloth); the rest of the project deserves one-half of the director's time.

It would be misleading to close on those notes. We all feel that the Consortium has been successful and we want to stay with it. As I explained earlier, the Consortium was conceived to serve our students. We think it has done that, and we think it has the potential to serve them better if we can keep it going. Not to appear altogether visionary and selfless, though, I think most of us would say, if backed into a corner, that we hope it will stay alive among us because we find it interesting and stimulating. We are glad that it benefits the students, but we would do Consortium things for their own sake. I think this means that the designer did his work well. A durable structure for education ought not to rely too much on visionary and selfless professors.

Chapter 5

Food, Land, and Power

POMONA COLLEGE
Claremont, California

Jerry A. Moles

The Problem

Agriculture influences everyone's life on a daily basis. Grain trade with the socialist bloc, for example, can affect the price of one of our primary staples, the bread we eat. Frost in Brazil makes our cup of coffee more expensive. DDT in meat produced in another country may cause a reduction in shipments to the United States and economic difficulties in the nation from which it originates.

Despite the significance of such day-to-day events on our lives, a personal concern for agriculture is not widespread in modern urban America. Few of America's young are exposed to the ways food is produced and distributed. Recognizing this problem, Pomona College initiated a program in Food, Land, and Power (FLP) in 1979. The effort, which received funding from the W. K. Kellogg Foundation, has been helping to increase people's agricultural literacy through a schedule of events and studies designed to raise the consciousness of Americans about agricultural issues. Through the program, faculty, students, and many people in the broader Southern California community have joined together to become students of agriculture in a changing world order.

The Setting

Pomona College is located 35 miles east of Los Angeles in what was once a major citrus and grape producing area (housing developments and freeways have gobbled up the orchards and

Jerry A. Moles was associate professor of anthropology and director of the Food, Land & Power program at Pomona College, Claremont, CA. He currently is scientific coordinator of The Institute of Sustainability, Davis, California, and research coordinator of the New Synthesis Research Centre, Mirahawatte, Sri Lanka.

vineyards in recent years). Students are drawn from across the United States and from a number of other countries. Selective in its admission policies, Pomona has gained wide recognition for its academic programs both on the campus and in domestic and overseas sites. The faculty is strongly committed to teaching and yet, annually, also produces an impressive list of publications and research endeavors. With the resources available on its campus and in the Los Angeles area, Pomona students have a rich educational experience.

As a liberal arts college, Pomona College was an ideal institution at which to initiate a FLP program. Each Pomona student, in the course of his or her educational experience, is exposed to the humanities; the arts; and the physical, biological, and social sciences. Pomona's sound liberal arts education presents fundamentals in many disciplines and encourages a broadness of vision in exploring important topics and issues.

A number of other factors placed Pomona College in an excellent position to promote agricultural literacy in the liberal arts. First, students, faculty, and people in the surrounding community were, and continue to be, supportive of its public affairs offerings. This provided an avenue for the introduction of materials on global food production, agricultural development and modernization, and the condition of international agricultural resources. Second, the College had an existing International Education program which extends campus boundaries to other nations. Not only did this program allow students to study at great colleges and universities of the world, it also made possible the formation of modular academies operated by Pomona faculty in a number of places. (Modular academies represent the moving of classrooms to places off campus where the surrounding environs contribute to the classroom presentations. Further, students are given access to resources which are not available in Claremont and Southern California. As a consequence, the Pomona campus is extended to a number of other countries and locations within the United States.) Third, the Pomona faculty was active in the governance of the College and, as a result, was willing to assume responsibility for oversight of the FLP program. Fourth, Pomona, which is one of the Claremont Colleges (Scripps, Claremont McKenna, Pitzer, Harvey Mudd, and the Claremont Graduate School) and which is adjacent to the School of Theology in Claremont, could call on members from a large faculty cluster of institutions to help advise them in the development and in implementation of the FLP program.

Further, the College's relationship with these institutions could expand the field of students who might participate in FLP activities. (Participation in the program also was enhanced by the College's relationship to nearby universities with strong agricultural emphasis, such as California State Polytechnic University and the University of California, Riverside.) The fifth point in Pomona's favor was that the College was well known as a host of major conferences on a variety of topics and, therefore, its audience base was already established for conferences on agricultural issues.

And, finally, Pomona College was located in the nation's most productive agricultural state. From the Imperial Valley on the Mexican border to the northern tip of the Sacramento Valley near the Oregon border, agricultural research, production, processing, and distribution help to define California's environmental, economic, political, and social character. This massive agricultural system has provided numerous opportunities to develop off-campus summer field experiences which give students an intimate view of the workings of modern agriculture.

Program Plan

In selecting the name "Food, Land, and Power" for the program, the steering committee, which guided the development and implementation of the pilot effort, chose the program's topical focuses. *Food* is produced for human consumption and is contrasted with feed which is produced for other species, some of which in turn becomes food. *Land* is the resource base for all agricultural production and while existing in a fixed amount, the arable land available for cultivation and grazing is decreasing due to nonagricultural uses and environmental degradation. *Power* refers to the social relations which govern agricultural decisions and the distribution of benefits and costs of agricultural activity.

Power has a second interpretation which is also relevant to agriculture. Since the demand for nonrenewable fossil fuels to increase productivity and to reduce human labor is continually increasing, power can be viewed as the capacity to stimulate biological growth and to provide work's energy inputs. Because people depend on fossil fuels to produce much of their food, the long-term sustainability of current methods of production is open to serious question.

The program, as originally designed, also was framed in the context of agriculture in a changing world order. This theme suggests there is more to agriculture than the production and distribution of food and fiber. Former U.S. Secretary of Agriculture Earl Butz once said, for instance, that food is a weapon, a way of achieving nonagricultural objectives. In Sri Lanka, discussions over the relative merits of energy intensive or traditional organic methods of production hinge on increasing national indebtedness. In Mexico, the continuing debate over the value of large-scale, capital-intensive production and smaller-scale, labor-intensive production demonstrates concerns about the relationship between agricultural methods and the welfare of rural residents. In Indonesia the government is attempting to placate urban residents by controlling the price of rice. All these examples illustrate a world order which is being shaped by a complex set of purposes for agriculture.

Given the focus of the FLP program, Pomona College established three objectives for the initiative in its proposal to the Kellogg Foundation. These were: (1) a deepening of Pomona's curricular treatment of agricultural issues through the development of new cross-disciplinary courses and agricultural modules in a number of existing courses in the social and natural sciences as well as in the humanities; (2) the broadening of general student knowledge about agricultural issues through a series of symposia and conferences; and (3) the enrichment of student experiences with agriculture through field tutorials.

Curricular treatment of agricultural issues

Prior to the arrival of a full-time director of the program in the fall semester of 1979-80, a steering committee reviewed Pomona's existing treatment of agriculture in the curriculum, with special attention paid to international agricultural development. While there were no courses with a primary focus on agriculture, a large number of existing courses dealt in substantive ways with aspects of food production. The majority of agriculture-linked courses was found in the social science departments with a special richness in the interdisciplinary field of international relations. A relatively large number of courses in the sciences and humanities were found to have relevant course materials, e.g., the environmental interrelationships of plants and the biology and chemistry of nitrogen fixation in biology courses; the cultural growth in a history course on Tudor and Stuart, England; and the origins of agriculture in a course on cultural geography.

With the funding of the FLP program, the faculty was alerted to a new concern of the College. Consequently, some courses were modified to include a deeper treatment of agriculture even before the program reached full stride. International Economics, Economic Development, and Cultural Geography were revised, for example, and a new three-semester core sequence in biology was introduced, relating ecology, organismal biology, and genetics in ways which permitted inclusion of agricultural topics.

Upon the arrival of a full-time director, a new interdepartmental course was offered on the structure of North American agriculture. In addition, the director lectured to existing courses not only on the Pomona campus, but also at other Claremont Colleges.

In order to assure a continuing flow of ideas in the curriculum, the steering committee invited faculty members to apply for summer support to prepare new courses and to create modules for existing courses. The committee decided to award three grants. Two went to the biology faculty to give students the opportunity to study the effects of different agroecosystems in a biochemical-oriented plant physiology course and to enable students to explore the available means of certain plant species, particularly the legumes, to bypass the need for nitrogen fertilizer through nitrogen fixation in a genetics course. The third award was made to an anthropologist to develop a course in food and nutrition in socio-cultural perspective. The director of the FLP program also prepared a course on small-scale agricultural producers in the Third World. The first year of program operations ended with three new courses and new agriculturally related modules in five single-semester courses and in the three-semester biology core sequence.

In the academic year 1980-81, the steering committee again sent out invitations for proposals and three awards were made. One grant permitted development of a module on agricultural land preservation in a government course on policy implementation and evaluation; the second grant was for a module to be included in Introduction to Social Anthropology covering subsistence systems, the evolution of food-production, and peasant society; and the third was to support preparation of a module in Cell Biology concerning the relationship between chloroplast and nuclear genomes and its influence on agricultural productivity. The director also developed courses for a Sri Lanka program scheduled to be conducted the following year. Courses included Community Research on Agricultural Systems, Food Policy and Agricultural Development, Intensive Sinlalese, and Introduction to Sri Lanka Culture and Agriculture. Appropriate supporting faculty members were to be found in Sri Lanka to help conduct the course. The director presented another new course on campus entitled Comparative Agricultural Development.

In the third year of the program, 1981-82, agricultural topics continued to increase in existing course offerings. A book on the international grain trade became required in one section of Issues in American Politics. An agricultural module was added to Introduction to International Relations. FLP funds were used for an anthropologist on the faculty to participate in a Massachusetts Institute of Technology training program in nutritional anthropology. (This same individual developed the course on food and nutrition in socio-cultural perspective at Pomona.) A government professor was partially supported for a trip to Viet Nam to explore changes in agricultural policy.

The development of new courses has led to changes in faculty research interests. The government professor who developed the module on agricultural land preservation is now engaged in a major research program investigating current changes in agricultural land use in California with the support of the state legislature. The director of the program has extended his research interests beyond the United States and Latin America and his last four professional papers have been concerned with Sri Lanka agricultural development. One of the papers was recently published in a Sri Lanka news magazine and led to an invitation to advise the Ministry of Agricultural Development and Research there.

Conferences and Symposia

The FLP program complemented the existing public events program being operated on the campus. The program funded presentations for classes on agricultural topics, provided speakers for the International Relations Colloquium, and sponsored speakers for presentations to broad campus and community audiences. The steering committee also planned major conferences in the third and fifth years of the program. Student, faculty, and community participation in all public events was encouraged through campus and local press, posters, direct invitation, and public announcements; these individuals were invited not only to be members of audiences but also to participate in the planning and direction of public presentations.

The following partial listing (See Appendix I for full listing.) of the speakers and their topics gives a clear indication of the nature of public presentations and of the range of material covered.

Mini conference on the "Size of Farms and the Quality of Life in Rural America," Walter Goldschmidt, professor of anthropology, University of California-Los Angeles; B. Delworth Gardner, professor agricultural economics, Berkeley and Davis campuses of the University of California, Director of the Gianninni Foundation; and E. Phillip LeVeen, economist, Public Interest Economics West, San Francisco.

"Mechanization, the University, and the Farm Workers" Ralph Abascal, chief counsel, California Rural Legal Assistance, Sacramento.

"Can a Botanist Wear Blinders? Externalities, Agriculture Policy and Crop Production" James P. Bennett, assistant professor of vegetable crops, University of California, Davis.

"International Agricultural Development: Perspectives from a Third World Biological Ecologist" Ranil Senanayake, National Heritage Trust and the Neo-synthesies Research Centre, Sri Lanka.

"Socioeconomic Development, Oil and Agriculture in Mexico" Jorge Calderon, economics faculty, National Autonomous University of Mexico.

"An Alternative Path of Development: Agricultural Sustainability Through Buddhist Wisdom as a Way of Life," and "Buddhist Thought in Action: Agrarian Reform and the National Heritage Trust"
C. Upali Senanayake, Sri Lankan Buddhist leader and agrarian reformer, founder of the National Heritage Trust of Sri Lanka.

"Nature and Madness — The Psychohistory of Human Ecology"
Paul Shepard, Avery professor of Human Ecology, Pitzer College.

The discussions that took place at these conferences during the first two years of the program raised a number of topics relating to both domestic and foreign agriculture. During the third year of the project these topics were summarized in a conference on "Agricultural Sustainability in a Changing World

Order." The purpose of the conference, which involved more than 60 national and international agricultural scientists, scholars, and land and soil experts, extended beyond stereotype images of agriculture. It was designed to give tomorrow's business and political leaders an understanding of the ideals and practicalities that someday may result in a hunger-free world. The conference at Pomona, attended by 300 people, provided a forum (See Appendix II for listing of principal conference papers.) to study ways to reduce future suffering caused by inadequate food supplies.

The "Agriculture Sustainability in a Changing World" conference demonstrated that Pomona College specifically, and liberal arts colleges in general, have something to offer not only students but also a broader community eager to understand agriculture. Since the time of the conference, even some of the lesser known speakers are being recognized as major voices shaping world agriculture futures. Sustainability is becoming a major topic of debate both nationally and internationally. The proceedings of the conference are now in book form as *Agricultural Sustainability in a Changing World Order*. A senior faculty member of another of the Claremont Colleges commented that the conference was the most significant community event of the last 15 years.

Enrichment of Student Experiences Through Field Tutorials

Given the rich opportunity available for the direct experiencing of agriculture, two field programs were organized to expand student awareness. The first program, organized for an eight-week summer session, has been operated on an annual basis. Students are invited to spend part of their vacation in the Winters-Davis area of Northern California in Solano and Yolo Counties. There they involve themselves in agricultural activities dispersed with interpretative sessions on their experiences and classroom presentations on related topics.

As a result of these summer field tutorials, students are able to contribute more fully to classroom discussions on agricultural topics and they better understand the relevancy of agriculture to everyday living. By harvesting tomatoes in the Sacramento Valley, for example, a discussion of labor inputs in agriculture becomes far more meaningful. When one backs a truck into a ditch or breaks a piece of equipment because of inexperience or careless-ness, that individual learns the consequences of actions. Daily life in the agricultural community has its frustrations and inconsis-tencies which are neither realized nor experienced in the class-room, yet it is in the context of daily life where the solutions to major problems are sought.

With the summer tutorials, the Pomona students developed an awareness of the magnitude and complexity of food production in one small locale in a very large nation in an even larger world. To some unknown and unknowable degree, they developed a deeper appreciation of the forces that govern agriculture in con-temporary America, of the nature of food production, and of the lives of their new friends in the agricultural community.

The second type of tutorial provided by the Food, Land, and Power program was semester-long study in Sri Lanka. This experience extended the program not only geographically but in magnitude of food and agricultural issues addressed. Upon arrival in the country, students are engaged in intensive classroom activities covering the history, agriculture, religion, and culture of the island nation. They then embark on a three-week tour of the island in which village life, the nation's agricultural history, its archaeology, agricultural practices, and ecological and agri-cultural regions are explored first-hand. Students transplant rice by hand, observe agricultural ceremonies which date back over 1,000 years, and walk paths where Sri Lankans have walked through their 2,300-year recorded history.

Immediately following the tour, students are assigned to households of farmers, the offices of agricultural researchers and administrators, and the fields and forests of the country to research interests which may have emerged as a result of their earlier activities and studies. In the past, students have mapped complex three-tiered forest gardens near Kandy; have explored nutrition, the agricultural cycle and calendar, and rituals which highlight the planting and harvesting cycles of a rice-producing village; have inquired into food distribution in the Dry Zone of the country; and have become involved in ongoing research programs operated by a variety of organizations and agencies. Consulting services are provided by two Pomona staff persons and a host of warm and supportive Sri Lanka professional people.

Each student produces two reports, one on the research project and a second on their personal reaction to the experience.

While no polished and publishable journal articles are likely to come from the experience, the awareness and care put forth in the papers demonstrates a vast appreciation for the difficulties of Third World agriculture and the magnitude of changes which must take place if current trends are to be reversed. In the personal statements, there are expressions of the realization of individual growth, and of newly discovered competency.

Program Organization

It is difficult to describe in simple terms how the program was organized. Initially a proposal was written to the Kellogg Foundation. Shortly thereafter interested faculty members organized themselves into a steering committee. The chairman of the Department of Economics became chair of the committee and a major voice on behalf of agriculture on the campus. He had administrative experience and through his long service to the College, was well known. Through a careful selection of colleagues representing interests from economics, government, sociology, anthropology, biology, and philosophy, a diverse and effective group of supporters was assembled. Steering committee members were directly involved in the debates which focused on the operation of the program, its educational content, and methods of presenting agriculture to the community.

The Pomona College's administration played a supportive and responsive role. All publicity was shared with the president's and dean's offices; senior administrative officers were invited to FLP functions; annual reports to the Kellogg Foundation were used as means of keeping the local administration informed. Further, when decisions were made requiring additional funding, personnel changes, or curricular modifications, the administration participated in the process.

Leadership for the program was provided by a temporary faculty member with experience in agriculture. The availability of such an individual from the outside helped shorten the planning stage of the project and generated a great deal of activity after the Kellogg Foundation funded the program. A problem created by the arrangement was the establishment of the position as a temporary role. That individual has since ceased to serve as the director of the project and there is need for additional leadership to come from among the existing faculty.

While the director and program assistant handled the day-to-day operations of the FLP program, the College's news bureau arranged publicity, made contact with news agencies, and handled the press in the special events sponsored by FLP. They also maintained a photographic record of the program's activities and wrote releases for the local and national press as well as for national newspapers of Sri Lanka. Further, they prepared features on the program for campus publications. The Public Information Office of the Claremont University Center and the Claremont Colleges assisted in publicity and the video laboratory of the School of Theology in Claremont helped record public events for later presentation to different audiences.

A student steering committee was formed with Pomona students and representatives from the other campuses. This group was very active in recruiting for off-campus programs; planning, publicizing, and directing public events; and organizing and operating an educational community garden on the campus. The off-campus programs were very important in developing student leadership. The most active students were those who had spent time in either Northern California or Sri Lanka. Participants in off-campus programs also presented their experiences through slide shows to the broader Claremont community and to the alumni council. Several students from the steering committee wrote articles which appeared in on-campus and local newspapers. The students also organized and produced *Seed Crystal,* a bulletin of the Food, Land, and Power program. (The bulletin is distributed in the Claremont community and to friends of the program within the United States and overseas. The outreach programs are dependent upon the farming communities where students are placed, the state government, the University of California, Sri Lanka, etc.; *Seed Crystal* helped maintain communication with this diverse audience.)

A number of Pomona faculty, both within and outside the steering committee, helped contact people to participate in program activities. Further, the director had a number of professional contacts within the agricultural community prior to coming to Pomona. With the assistance of other faculty members, he placed students in off-campus programs, thereby helping to tie the program to the broader community.

Process and Product

While process and product are terms which suggest causality and predictable consequence, most educators know that it is difficult to think minutely about the continuous daily actions that give vision and understanding to phenomena. Within the context of the FLP program, it is difficult to know the exact cause of learning, insight, or creativity. And yet students change. Some turn their career objectives toward agriculture and natural resources management. Others take up gardening, and still others return to visit faculty members in order to continue their agricultural education. While it is difficult to be specific about the causes of educational change, these indicators suggest the process is working.

Among the records left by the students are the thesis topics each student selects during the senior year. The topics represent areas of particular concern which are explored more systematically than any earlier academic work. The list which follows illustrates the students' breadth of interest and depth of inquiry:

a double major in Biology and Contemporary Agricultural Planning wrote two theses - one based on biological experimentation and analysis of cancer cells, the other focusing on agricultural policy and the family farm;

an anthropology major studied women in development;

an international relations major wrote "On Not Seeing the Forest for the Trees: The Importance of Forestry in Development";

a history major studied "Water Development and Allocation in the West: The Role of the Roosevelt Administration in the Building of the Los Angeles Aqueduct";

an anthropology major examined Nigerian market women and development;

a philosophy major wrote of "Thoughts on the Land: A Warning for the Future";

an international relations major explored "Development: A Process of Human Evolution — A Contextual Analysis of the Green Revolution";

still another international relations major wrote about "Development of Food Policy in India and China";

an anthropology major examined "Anthropometric Measurements and Nutritional Status Assessment"; and

a special major in Development and Social Change in the Third World developed a thesis on "Development and the Green Revolution: Agricultural Systems and Cultural Values."

Changes in activities by persons is another standard measure of change. Such changes have certainly been obvious in terms of faculty interaction across traditional boundaries dividing the humanities and natural and social sciences; between the various Claremont Colleges and the School of Theology at Claremont; and among state-supported institutions with concentrations in agricultural subjects. These relationships represent the foundation of an agricultural interest community. Faculty now engage more frequently in agriculturally related research and agricultural concerns are presented in a wide variety of courses. Faculty have found positions on advisory boards to foundations, national and state governments, and to other colleges and universities.

As the faculty changed, so did the students. Some Pomona students began searching for careers in new areas of interest. Former participants in FLP now hold agriculturally related positions in state government, special interest educational organizations, Peace Corps, agricultural marketing, and in farming. Others have continued their agricultural interests in graduate school.

As a consequence of student participation in Northern California and Sri Lanka, new interest communities have been formed. California farmers met with land-grant university faculty and representatives of state government. Sri Lanka cultivators met embassy and national government officials and the exponents of growth — those who suggest more buildings, dams, etc. — met their environmental critics who believed unchecked industrial approaches to agriculture would destroy the biological productive capacity of the nation's natural resources. Friendships emerged and, after the Pomona students left, new relationships continued. Supporters of the program frequently ask when students will return and whether they will participate again on their farm, in their office, or at the University experimental station. The program has touched the lives of thousands of persons through these activities, again, with noticeable educational consequences.

Lessons Learned

Upon a review of the past five years, a number of experiences stand out. First, the lengthy discussions with both faculty and students steering committees seemingly eliminated major or costly failures. This is not to say that all components of the program worked perfectly the first or even the second time. Nor does it mean that all faculty contact led to strong support and participation or that all students were delighted with the hard work on farms or travel in Sri Lanka. Rather, it indicates that, despite miscues along the way, the involvement of faculty and students in planning the FLP program helped make the project more appealing and meaningful for all involved.

Second, having a director come in from the outside had both positive and negative aspects. The lack of familiarity with his colleagues and the political lay of the land started the new program director off with major informational needs. The steering committee served admirably in providing a hasty "enculturation and socialization." The new director's experience in agriculture brought, on the other hand, valuable information regarding the field. He was able to focus the program on key issues in agriculture with a minimal amount of time and energy spent on research and resource development.

A third lesson is that a knowledge of the existing administrative and faculty routines and decision-making process is important. A new program must blend with the forces that structure the college. A knowledge of the institution's factions and cohorts assists in the interpretation of events and placement of information about agriculture. Who on the faculty, for instance, is interested in agricultural land, resources, degradation, international agricultural trade, etc.? Persons with similar interests are likely to associate together and, when one or two are found, they can direct you to others.

Fourth, staying in touch with a support group is critical. Monthly steering committee meetings for both faculty and students, informal discussions about agriculture, guest lectures in other classes by the director and steering committee members, special events, and major conferences kept the program viable to the community. The small core group of students who helped make the program a living phenomenon on the campus met frequently in the FLP office. Most of them shared rich experiences in Northern California and Sri Lanka in addition to their experiences on campus. Having a meeting place that was distinctly FLP was helpful. The administrative assistant of the program, one of its strongest supporters, helped nurture the FLP program. She served not only as an administrator of the effort but as a campus spokesperson on agriculture as well.

The sixth lesson learned was that off-campus tutorials are enriching and, at times, frustrating. The greatest amount of excitement was generated by the tutorials. Life directions were changed. For example, an international relations major, after two years in rice production in Africa, is now entering Princeton University to study agricultural development and government in developing nations. In addition special majors were designed, thesis topics were explored through first-hand investigation, and classroom information was interpreted in a new and more sophisticated manner. At the same time, not all students were able to adjust equally well to hand labor, office boredom, and tropical heat. Nor were they equally pleased with their experiences. Nevertheless, there was strong student support for the tutorials and those few people who claimed not to like the experience maintain that they learned from the activity. The special moments and items in students' lives that these opportunities afforded made up for the inevitable hardship and discomfort. Fortunately, most Pomona students were stimulated by the challenges and responded beautifully.

Perhaps the biggest lesson learned was that it is difficult to integrate even a very successful curricular innovation into the ongoing programmatic structure of a liberal arts college. As long as outside resources not previously tapped can be used to support new ideas, it is relatively easy to adapt existing programs to accommodate new features of agricultural awareness. No doubt many of these adaptations will continue as part of the curricular life of the college as long as the faculty members responsible for them remain and their interest in models of agricultural change stays high. But they need a support system which will nurture and broaden these interests, and that system must contain effective organizations as well as the commitment of resources for its continuance.

As the steering committee contemplated the end of the Kellogg Foundation support (in the summer of 1984), it drew up plans for several alternative means of renewing interest in the FLP program at the College. It considered a "business as usual" model, since the existing program structures seem to have worked well during the "start-up" period. But it was rejected after further consideration because of its image as a temporary program dependent on outside funding and its ambiguous claim on a place in the Pomona College curriculum; these liabilities made it vulnerable to a degree of uncertainty that neither its staunchest supporters nor its staff could any longer tolerate.

A second model, involving creation of an interdisciplinary concentration, also was finally rejected because it implied a degree of expertise about agriculture in the Pomona College faculty which really does not, even yet, exist. It was also rejected because its methods of investigation still would be very experimental and eclectic — a fatal liability at a College like Pomona — and because its implementation would commit the College to a level of support which cannot be fully justified just yet.

A third model, involving the addition of Food, Land, and Power concerns to existing concentrations, is probably the most coherent structure considered. But it too was rejected, primarily for two reasons. The first was that it would have proven to be the hardest option to implement, since bringing it to curricular life would require extensive negotiations with several departments in addition to the normal procedures for approving new curricular options. The other reason, once again, was financial. This option would have required the retention of a program director who not only would teach essential courses in particular parts of the curriculum and would give overall guidance to the program, but who also would be adept at carrying on the delicate negotiations with individual departments implied in the model. Administrative assistance in setting up the FLP colloquia, organizing internships, and maintaining appropriate records would have added appreciably to the budget.

The option finally chosen during the last year of Kellogg support required the incorporation of the FLP program into the international relations concentration. The College's international relations program, especially during the last decade, has come to be the most popular interdisciplinary program at the College. And as it has grown, student interest in particular aspects of the major have diverged, creating the opportunity to develop parallel "tracks" or thematic groups of courses. The international relations committee now thinks that a focus on international development within the international relations concentration would provide an important thematic link between courses taught from different disciplinary vantage points, and ensure that the integration of these approaches involved more than an introduction to the fundamentals of economics, government and history for each international relations student. Development problems are intrinsically interdisciplinary because they involve an understanding of the cultural determinants, the historical trajectory, the economics factors, and the political restraints which are indispensable elements in the development process.

To a large extent, the FLP program has already been serving as a means of enriching and better coordinating College offerings in development studies since its interests in international agricultural development have animated most of what we have done in the past few years. Thus a healthy working relationship already existed between the international relations committee and FLP steering committee (six members of which are common to both committees).

Pomona College is not suggesting the FLP concerns cease to exist as an identifiable feature of its curricular offerings. Rather, it is suggesting that they become a part of the academic and administrative structure of the international relations program, and their scope be broadened somewhat to include all aspects of international development and narrowed in other ways to include aspects of U.S. policies only to the extent they impinge directly on the processes of international development. Thus, the highly successful field study programs mounted each summer in the Davis-Winters section of the Sacramento Valley probably cannot be justified in the new configuration; instead, additional education opportunities in developing countries will be urged on by the education abroad committee.

The resource implications of this new modeling for FLP concerns are considerably more modest than the level of support that has been received from the Kellogg Foundation. They do not provide for continuance of a full-time director, nor do they support the program of internships in Northern California which have been such a vital part of the program in the past. But they do include funds for public events and curricular materials, and they permit Pomona College to continue a policy of encouraging faculty members with modest summer grants to adopt courses for insights about international agricultural development. Provision for a half-time administrative assistant to the international relations program and for office space and supplies also seems likely. Finally, the education abroad director is actively seeking additional opportunities for students in developing countries — opportunities which may be self-supporting rather than place additional demands on limited budget allocations.

Thus the Food, Land, and Power program is reasonably assured of a place in the College curriculum for the indefinite future, but surely not at the level of activity experienced during its initial five years. The decision of the College administration not to continue a director's position in the program implies the need to "internalize" supervision of program initiatives, as seems likely in the international relations committee context. By the same token, it means the loss from the faculty of the only fully-trained professional in the field.

Clearly, the longer-term future requires several faculty members to step forward with generous investments of time and energy to continue their work, seeing that students gain an appreciation for the knowledge and activities that sustain their very lives.

Chapter 6

Understanding the Rural Perspective

BRIAR CLIFF COLLEGE
Sioux City, Iowa

Sister Margaret Wick

The Problem

The quality of life in a society may depend more on successful agriculture than on any other activity. The resources of land, water, and air are easily exploited if there is not enough awareness of the need to preserve the fragile earth and its precarious agricultural enterprise. Agriculture has always embraced social values such as stewardship, loyalty, family, reverence, responsibility, and trust. Clearly, the goods and values of agriculture are life sustaining, and the farmer cannot bear responsibility for them alone. He must be supported by a sympathetic and informed people who realize that his best interest is theirs as well.

Briar Cliff College's "Heartland" program for the appreciative study of agriculture is one attempt to increase awareness of and commitment to agriculture. The broad goals of the program are to:

introduce students to the variety, diversity, and complexity of agriculture;

study the profound interdependence of agriculture with national and world economics and nutrition;

observe the fragility of the American farm as an economic and environmental unit, and to assess the resulting need to preserve and protect it;

promote concern for the quality of personnel and social life in rural areas, especially in the light of declining rural populations and their endangered institutions;

explore the possibilities for reintegrating rural and urban lifestyles; and, finally,

reaffirm the unique and historic contributions of agriculture to American life in the hope of maintaining them in the face of change.

Sister Margaret Wick is academic dean at Briar Cliff College, Sioux City, IA.

The Setting

Briar Cliff College is a Catholic, Franciscan, coeducational college of approximately 1,000 students. The College is located in Sioux City, Iowa (population: 85,000). The geographic location of the College, its clientele, and specific features of its history and mission all contributed to the success of its agricultural appreciation program.

Sioux City, Iowa, the northernmost port on the Missouri River, has played an increasingly important role in the shipping and exporting of grain. The stockyards have significantly affected the promotion and development of a series of related industries, from feedlot operations to meat processing plants and commodities brokerages. Sioux City is also on the boundary between two distinct forms of agriculture: the prairie type, extending eastward and favoring corn, soybeans, and feedlots; and the high plains type, extending westward and comprising alfalfa, grassland range, and cattle ranching. Consequently, Sioux City has been an advantageous location for the development of a diversity of agricultural-related industries: Iowa Beef Processors, Terra Chemicals International, the Sioux City Stockyards, Big Soo Grain Terminal, and American Popcorn Company.

Briar Cliff College, founded in 1930 by the Sisters of St. Francis, has been a regional college since its beginning. Most of its students come from farms, small towns, or medium-sized cities that are agricultural-dependent.

Several aspects of the College's tradition and mission were influences on the agriculture program. The College's Franciscan tradition places importance on reverence for all of creation and on service. In recent years, the Catholic Church, through a group of midwest bishops, issued a statement on stewardship of land. The College views itself as a "community among communities" and has a sense of public service — perhaps more than is typical among private, liberal arts colleges.

These factors — geographic location, clientele, and tradition — were influential in the design and implementation of the program. One would have thought at first glance that Briar Cliff would not need such a program. The College found, however, that attitudes toward, and awareness of, agricultural issues are perhaps most unexamined by those who live in the midst of agricultural abundance.

Program Plan

Briar Cliff's "Heartland" program was based on two assumptions: existing curriculum structures would be used and all faculty in all departments would be eligible to participate.

The curriculum structure used for this program was the College's minicourse/independent research course. This curriculum components consists of a series of one-credit courses designed to provide timely, flexible, educational experiences. Students are required to take one minicourse per term for each of three terms during the freshman and sophomore years. At the junior and senior level the one-credit courses are called independent research and are taken within the department of a student's major. This curriculum feature then allows for diversity and flexibility as well as for indepth study of special topics within the area of each student's concentration.

In September of the first year of the program, an open invitation was issued to all departments to submit minicourse and independent research course proposals related to agricultural and food issues. The intent of the grant was fully explained. Twelve of the 17 departments responded with a total of 22 course proposals involving 20 faculty members. As the program developed and was implemented over three years, 21 courses were actually taught. These courses came from 11 different departments and involved 18 faculty members.

The courses were grouped for purposes of publicity under four themes: rural services, rural culture, rural business/technology/ecology, and national/international issues. A brief description of each follows:

Rural Services

EDUCATION: TEACHING IN RURAL SCHOOLS IN THE 80s

This minicourse was designed for students interested in teaching in rural schools. Through readings, interviews, visits to rural schools, and review of the various associations of rural schools, students explore the problems, advantages, and disadvantages of rural education.

NURSING: RURAL NURSING

This course explored the health care needs of a rural population and the unique characteristics of nursing practice in a rural setting. This course was offered once in workshop format and once in regular format with a clinical component at a nearby Indian reservation.

SOCIOLOGY/SOCIAL WORK: RURAL HUMAN SERVICES

Using texts and readings supplemented by visits to rural agencies, students increased awareness of rural human services. They also visited a rural community to determine the "natural helping network." These networks form outside of the formal social service system and consist of persons who are good listeners: friends, teachers, ministers, bartenders, hairdressers, barbers, etc. This course was offered once in regular format and was supplemented once by a workshop on Rural Human Services.

SOCIOLOGY/SOCIAL WORK: THE ELDERLY IN RURAL IOWA

The purpose of this course was to examine programs and services which rural communities provide for their elderly and to critique these offerings. Readings were supplemented by field trips to small towns near Sioux City. This course was offered once as an independent research course for majors, and once as a unit within a more extensive course on the elderly.

SOCIOLOGY/SOCIAL WORK: RURAL WOMEN

The common concerns and issues of rural women were reviewed in this course. Interviews with rural women, readings, and participation in a workshop on rural women provided learning experiences in the course.

SOCIOLOGY/SOCIAL WORK: RURAL SOCIAL POLICY

A general sociological analysis of American farming — past, present, and future — was presented in this offering. It also examined the ways farming is affected by the interplay of economics, political, and social policies. Readings, films, and speakers from area agricultural policy centers were learning tools for this course.

THEOLOGY: RURAL MINISTRY IN THE 80s

This course was designed to put the gospel into rural terms and consequently into rural life. It also encouraged future rural ministers to get involved in the real issues of the community in which they minister. Recent church publications on rural issues and ministry were read, films were viewed, and ministers from rural areas were invited as guest lecturers.

Rural Culture

ENGLISH: HOMESTEADING

The possibilities and values of homesteading — the post-modern, small farm, do-it-yourself lifestyle — were explored in this course. Homesteading was considered as an alternative to either urban dependency or full-time commercial farming. Reading and discussion were supplemented by visits to homesteading sites.

ENGLISH: HEARTLAND: THE LAND, THE PEOPLE, AND LITERATURE

Students read and discussed novels, nonfiction, and poetry that embody the people's relationship to the land in the 19th and 20th centuries in this course. Focus was on authors who lived or wrote about areas near Sioux City. Field trips to local museums supplemented readings.

HISTORY: THE U.S. FARMER'S HERITAGE

An overview of the social trends in the history of farming from colonial times to 1850 was given. Relationships between the period studied and the foundations of farming in the heartland were drawn, and appreciation for the contributions of early farming was emphasized. Reading, films, slides, and a visit to the Living History Farms in Des Moines were learning activities in this course.

MASS COMMUNICATIONS: RURAL PHOTOGRAPHY, AN EXAMINATION OF FSA PHOTOGRAPHERS

Students were given background on the Farm Security Administration and its photographers who documented the rural areas of America during the Depression. Microfiche slides were available for study. The slides were also indexed by topic so they could be used for other purposes.

SPEECH/THEATRE: HISTORY OF RURAL THEATRE

This course grew out of research on the type of theatrical or paratheatrical entertainment available to the rural Iowan from 1857-1900. Its focus after three years has become the rural opera house. Students review original sources and visit facilities that still exist.

SOCIOLOGY/SOCIAL WORK: AGRICULTURAL FOLKLORE IN RURAL NORTHWEST IOWA

This effort trained sociology majors in the research method of ethnography. A small town near Sioux City was selected; interviews of residents sensitized students to the broad range of norms and sayings which constitute the folklore of rural towns.

Rural Business/Technology/Ecology

BIOLOGY: AGRO-ECOLOGY OF NORTHWEST IOWA
An overview of the first 100 years of agriculture was given in this course. The ecology of native vegetation and the development of a two-crop system were also studied. Field trips and guest speakers supplemented readings.

BIOLOGY: ALTERNATIVE AGRICULTURES
Offered in workshop format, the course examined the environmental and economic problems of American agriculture. National speakers, panels of experts, and persons involved in alternative methods were resources for the workshop/course.

BIOLOGY: DISAPPEARING GRASSLANDS
Background knowledge of grassland ecology, plants found in natural prairies, and the effect of grazing on natural grasslands were provided in this course. Field study of prairies was an important part of the endeavor.

MATH/COMPUTER SCIENCE: COMPUTERS IN AGRICULTURE
Various ways by which farmers can make their operations more efficient and productive were considered in this class. Students used microcomputers and software which examined profit and loss, nonprofitable animals, and use of government information to predict prices.

BUSINESS/ACCOUNTING: AGRICULTURE AND TAXATION
Students learned how the tax structure relates to fiscal policy and impacts on agriculture. Focus was on income tax, gift and estate taxes, and property taxes. Guest speakers were used to add expertise in some of the agricultural applications.

National/International Issues

MASS COMMUNICATIONS: MINORITIES IN AGRICULTURE
The contributions of ethnic and racial minority farmers to the American way of life was the focus of this effort. Groups studied were the Amana, American Indian, Amish, French-Canadian, and

Mexican American. Videotaping at on-site locations was the medium used as a learning tool. An outcome of this course was a completed documentary-style production.

SOCIOLOGY/SOCIAL WORK: THIRD WORLD AGRICULTURE

Through readings, lectures, and films students became aware of the agricultural practices and problems of developing countries. They developed standards and skills to evaluate the suitability of labor intensive modes of agricultural productions and became sensitized to roles the United States might play in the development of agriculture in the Third World countries.

SOCIOLOGY/SOCIAL WORK: LAND USE ISSUES IN AGRICULTURAL AMERICA

Through reading and the use of census data to map out changing land use patterns, students identified basic forces behind changing land use patterns in rural America and evaluated the pros and cons of the family farm.

Over the three-year period of the grant the various mini-courses and independent research courses were scheduled a total of 40 times, i.e., an average of twice for each course.

Another component of the program was a series of special symposia and workshops. These events grew out of the College's public service and outreach tradition and were designed to serve persons not enrolled at the College as traditional students. A list of special events is given below:

"Perspectives on the Family Farm" — Cosponsored with the Sioux City Diocesan Coalition for the Preservation of the Family Farm, the symposium presented perspectives of new and experienced farmers, politicians, church and college personnel.

"Land for Food and People" — This symposium consisted of four days of events, including academic speakers, simulation games, music and drama.

"Perspectives on Rural American Women" — The conference featured a national speaker and area women who were involved in farming or served rural women.

"Rural Human Services: Issues for the 80s" — A keynote address on rural legislative issues was followed by various concurrent workshops on counseling and value systems, Native Americans, peace and agriculture, rural elderly, and rural play.

"Rural Women: Unspoken Issues in Rural Areas" — This second workshop for women featured regional speakers and round table discussions on various issues of concern to women.

"Computers on the Farm: The Newest Hired Hand" — The workshop introduced farmers to the applications of personal computers on the farm. A group of farmers currently using computers discussed their experience, and a "hands-on" session was provided.

"Alternatives for Agriculture: What Will Work?" — The problems and future implications of the continued use of present farming methods were discussed by a national speaker, panel of experts, and group of farmers engaged in such alternate farming methods as organic farming, minimum till farming, and nonchemical farming.

Program Organization

The organization of the "Heartland" project was implemented with relative ease because existing curriculum and administrative structures were used. Basically, this was a faculty-centered project, yet the faculty did not perceive it as an "extra" request or complain about administrative details. This was accomplished by giving faculty members a reason and means for becoming involved.

The Office of the Academic Dean assumed responsibility for the administration and implementation of the program. All interested faculty submitted course proposals to the Academic Affairs Committee, the group which ordinarily approves new courses. Virtually all proposals were accepted, with suggestions given for revision in some cases.

Two consultants were brought to campus who had experience in similar programs. One visited during the course development stage and inspired several good course ideas among faculty members. The second consultant spent time on campus after the courses were approved but before they had been fully developed. Again, this provided an opportunity for faculty members to visit with an "expert" from another campus and to talk to each other about their courses.

During the summer between the first and second years of the grant, faculty members were invited to apply for "mini-sabbaticals." This provided financial support to develop the courses. Summer activity took faculty to rural areas for work, interviews, and research. Some faculty attended conferences on topics related to their course; others traveled to area research libraries. Activities were as varied as the courses and faculty members. At the conclusion of the summer, a day-long meeting was held with all participating faculty members. They reported summer activities and explained how these activities would have an impact on course development.

As courses were implemented it became even more important to schedule activities which would bring participating faculty together. At the end of each term and at the beginning of each academic year, the 18 faculty members met to update each other on activities and research related to their courses. These sessions were supplemented by several field trips to area farms or rural historical sites. Participating faculty members attended the special event workshops and were invited to classes when special guest lecturers visited. In summary, the identity of the participating faculty as a group involved in a common project became an important component of the program. Although they were teaching independent courses, they became aware of common issues and interdisciplinary perspectives.

Publicity about the program, both on and off campus, was important to give the "Heartland" project identity as a program rather than as a series of courses. As soon as courses were approved, an attractive brochure was prepared to publicize the program. An on-campus newsletter also was published four times each year and distributed to all College personnel. These activities kept the program visible even to those not directly involved.

Local newspapers, radio, and television stations gave good coverage to the total program, to specific courses, and to special events. This publicity brought inquiries and enrollment for courses and workshops.

To reiterate: the regular academic channels for the College were followed for course approval; faculty taught courses as part of their regular load and received funds for summer course development activities; and the program was publicized and perceived as a total institutional program. These components of organization contributed to "Heartland's" success.

Process and Product

Just how successful was Briar Cliff's Kellogg program? Some of the effects are easily quantifiable:

Twenty-one credit courses have been developed. These courses come from 11 different departments, representing two-thirds of the College's departments.

Eighteen faculty members developed and taught program courses; this represents 30 percent of the College's faculty.

Over the three-year period, these courses were scheduled a total of 40 times, i.e., an average of twice for each course.

Enrollment in courses over the three-year period totaled 300 students. During these years, the College's full-time equivalent enrollment averaged 1,000. This means that approximately 30 percent of the College's students have enrolled in a "Heartland" course.

In addition to courses, nine special events were held. Attendance at these totaled approximately 950 persons.

It is difficult, however, to quantify the real impact of the program. It has had its greatest effect on the faculty who designed, developed, and implemented new courses. It enabled them to: (1) develop expertise in a new area of their discipline; (2) acquire library, learning center, and equipment needed for the course; (3) communicate with colleagues in other disciplines about a common topic; and (4) become aware of external groups and persons who will continue to provide resources for their courses. Faculty members learned about agriculture from their discipline perspective, but this perspective contributed to and was shaped by the cross-disciplinary emphasis of the total program.

Students learned about agriculture from the perspective of a single discipline. For most, courses provided an opportunity to focus on a topic that related to their rural backgrounds. One would hope that these perspectives, although isolated, have led them to view their discipline and their rural heritage in a new way.

The impact of the program on the total College and on community participants was mutually reinforcing. Because of good publicity, particularly concerning the special events, the region began to look to Briar Cliff for leadership in agricultural topics. A mailing list kept the community informed; in turn, the community asked the College to participate in civic, corporate, and church-related projects. A concrete result of the program is that an informal network of organizations concerned with rural topics has emerged. Because the College's perspective is broader than any one of the single organizations, it is natural for it to become the coordinating body.

In summary, Briar Cliff's "Heartland" project has changed the College because it has changed 30 percent of its faculty. Courses now reflect a new awareness and sensitivity to the field of agriculture. Rural life and its issues have become a part of the liberal arts curriculum and the outreach services of the College.

Lessons Learned

Much of what worked in the "Heartland" project was not preplanned. Coordination by the Academic Dean's office gave the program clout when needed, facilitated implementation of details, and kept any one of the courses from "stealing the show." Bringing the participating faculty together for formal and informal meetings kept lines of communication open among them and served as an opportunity to generate new and often cross-disciplinary ideas. The fact the faculty members were quite autonomous in course development and implementation activities definitely contributed to the positive impact on faculty. However, if there had not been strong (but tolerant) central "control," this autonomy may have led to fragmentation of the program.

Fragmentation did occur if one looks at the program from a student perspective. Three hundred students took "Heartland" courses. Often, they were not aware that the course they were taking was part of a larger program; they did not know who the other students were in other courses. Several times the faculty talked about ways to build a support group of students who had taken these courses, or to identify them publicly by selling T-Shirts with the logo.

Networking among various rural organizations could have been formalized. The idea of a "finale" workshop, one bringing together all groups concerned about agriculture, was discussed but never materialized. Families of students, a potential part of this network, were neglected.

When courses were developed it might have been good to "tie them back" more closely to the goals. Perhaps now it would be wise to hold a conference at the College with a session focused on each goal, drawing on the talent that has been developed.

The "Heartland" project goes on because the courses have become part of departmental offerings. In the first year without funding, one-third of the courses were scheduled and a workshop, "Rural Women III" was planned.

If one assumes that new institutional awareness is conveyed to students, then it seems that Briar Cliff students will leave the College better informed and prepared to be reflective on agricultural issues.

Chapter 7

Food, Peace, and International Development

WILMINGTON COLLEGE
Wilmington, Ohio

David Parsons

The Problem

In the early 1960s, Wilmington College was one of the few liberal arts colleges in the United States that offered a four-year agriculture program. That major, which has grown substantially since, was and continues to be designed to prepare students for careers in production agriculture, agribusiness, agriscience, and vocational education. But while students graduated from the program with strong agricultural skills, they frequently did not fully understand the relationship of agriculture to society. Students graduating in Wilmington's traditional liberal arts programs had an even lesser grasp of the interrelatedness of agriculture to the environment, cultural traditions, political systems, and social values. Many did not know the fundamentals of how food, feed, and fiber products are actually produced, processed, and marketed. Even those individuals with an interest in the issues of peace and international development had only limited knowledge of the crucial role food plays in the resolution of these problems.

Recognizing this fact, several Wilmington College faculty members designed a plan to establish a program to make it possible for students, faculty, and surrounding community groups to learn more about the connectedness of agricultural activities to global events. This novel experiment was funded by the W. K. Kellogg Foundation in 1980.

The Setting

Wilmington College was in a particularly advantageous position

David Parsons is director of the Food, Peace, and International Development program at Wilmington College, OH.

to develop and implement an agriculture-in-the-liberal arts program. Founded in 1870 by the Religious Society of Friends (Quakers), it has long had close ties to the thriving agricultural communities of southwestern Ohio. (Many of the earliest settlers of the area were Quakers, a number of them from the Carolinas who emigrated as their opposition to slavery grew.)

The College describes itself as:

...a career-oriented coeducational liberal arts college, with a Quaker tradition of peace, service, and inner direction, and a special interest in the community in which it is located and in smaller communities and organizations generally. Wilmington seeks to equip students of all ages for careers and leadership roles; ...to provide special services, including cultural and research facilities and continuing education programs, to the communities and organizations of the area; and to prepare people of all ages for leadership and service roles in Friends' organizations and similar agencies.

Reflecting another Quaker concern for world peace, Wilmington has a Peace Resource Center and a Peace Studies program. It also offers a variety of courses with an international focus, employs a faculty with considerable international experience, and annually enrolls about 50 international students, many from "developing" countries.

Wilmington's agricultural program, today with about 130 majors (total College enrollment is approximately 800), has used the College's diversified farm operations — the College owns some 1,000 acres of farmland — as a practical educational setting, giving agriculture students "hands-on" experience difficult to match even in a land-grant university.

Program Plan

Recognizing these assets, Wilmington's first step in program planning was to ascertain from department heads what courses might, with or without modification, fit a "Food, Peace, and International Development" theme. Working with this inventory, the program designers then came up with proposed additions, changes, and overall "rationalization" of courses required to meet the objectives they had in mind. Their plan involved revisions for approximately 10 courses, designed to serve as the nucleus of a "general education option" available to all students. (Wilmington's "Individualized Educational Planning" for students, set up in the climate of the late 1960s, had eliminated collegewide course requirements to give students more responsibility in planning their education. By the late 1970s, however, faculty were reconsidering this decision and deciding to reinstitute at least distribution requirements.) Five additional new courses were conceived — Global Dynamics, Human Nutrition, International Food Markets, Agricultural Policy Issues, and a hands-on farm practicum for nonagriculture majors — to serve as a core around which the revised courses would be grouped.

A second element of the program's design was a public lecture series, keyed to the new Agricultural Policy Issues course. Speakers from agricultural and development organizations were to be selected and asked to address a variety of issues, thereby helping the community to see agriculture in a broader context. Transcripts of the lectures and course syllabi were to be made available to regional organizations and other educational institutions, and used in active, promotional efforts. The emphasis on community outreach stemmed from the realization that student "agricultural illiteracy" was a reflection of a more general societal failure to make connections. It was clearly an important, if formidable, task to stimulate change in the social context, as well as in the education of students from that context.

Program design also included employment of a full-time, outside "coordinator" and (half-time) support staff to provide leadership in the program's implementation; an admissions staffperson to promote the program with prospective students; a practicum instructor to design and manage that new course; a "community outreach" coordinator to organize speakers, workshops, etc. with community groups; and a secretary. Working with a faculty team, the coordinator and staff would: review selected courses and plan ways to enrich and integrate them; identify important agricultural policy issues and select speakers to discuss them; and plan outreach and marketing strategies for the program.

Food, Peace, and International Development (FPID) was primarily targeted at students. By gradually integrating new and revised courses into the College curriculum, it was hoped that the number of students interested in the program, for career or intellectual reasons, would grow and make the program self-sustaining.

Organization

The program was laid out on a three-and-a-half-year time schedule, to begin in May 1980. Following is a review of the broad outlines of that plan. During the first year, a program coordinator and part-time secretary were to be hired, and an advisory committee appointed. Coordinator and committee members were to select courses for revision and plan for and hold two summer workshops — one for 10 faculty to meet for two weeks to review courses, plan revisions, review agricultural policy issues, and plan program outreach and marketing; the other, for the faculty who would teach Global Dynamics to work out course plans. An amended design suggested by WKKF also called for a series of public workshops, seminars, short courses, and talks for community groups "staffed by people now on the College staff and others (and) . . . carried out by a part-time special coordinator."

During the first full development year, revised courses were to be offered and promoted throughout fall, winter, and spring quarters. The person who handled admissions was to develop materials and presentations on FPID and its career preparation aspects. During the school year, instructors for farm practicum and Human Nutrition were to develop those courses for subsequent quarters. The program coordinator was expected to teach Agricultural Policy Issues and to set up the public lecture series linked to the course.

During the second full year, another summer faculty workshop was scheduled. An International Food Markets course was to be prepared. All five of the new courses were then to be offered during the school year. The program coordinator and an admissions person were to work throughout the year on outreach and marketing, using materials from the lecture series, and involving students in off-campus presentations.

During the final year, a third summer faculty workshop with the original group and two outside consultants was slated to evaluate the program in relation to the total curriculum. During the year, the five new courses and seven revised courses were to be offered. The coordinator and admissions person were to continue recruiting and conducting outreach activities.

Process and Product

Wilmington's FPID program effectively got underway with the hiring of a coordinator in April 1981. Based on this timing, the coordinator (1) began an assessment of existing campus resources — books, periodicals, films — on agriculture/development/peace topics; (2) sought out contacts with a wide range of faculty and began planning for the first faculty summer workshop; and (3) wrote a one-page statement describing its FPID program and sent it with a cover letter soliciting advice and support to nearly 100 agencies and institutions with agriculture/development/peace interests.

The first faculty summer workshop committed participants to doing two weeks of independent research during the summer and to meeting and discussing results of that research at the summer's end. Faculty were to investigate how specific courses they taught could be modified to include consideration of agriculture or food-related issues. Ten faculty members from seven disciplines participated. They spent two weeks discussing with their colleagues what they had done, and using the preview of provocative films on food issues as a stimulus for discussion. (Economic concentration, chemicals and the environment, reasons for world hunger, and political uses of food were some of those issues. Discussions were taped for future reference.)

Faculty evaluations of the workshop were so positive that the same format was used the following year. However, the group attending that workshop was different in makeup. Specifically, it was comprised of individuals from a variety of campus interests. This broader involvement was seen as a means of institutionalizing the program. Those most logically central to the program — Agriculture, Peace Studies, and International Studies — at this point saw their interests as competing, rather than complementary.

The second workshop generated less excitement than the first. The group was smaller and the more enthusiastic faculty had already been selected the first year. Nonetheless, the second workshop may have been more successful, simply because it did have an impact on "hard-core" liberal arts people who initially saw no connection between themselves and FPID.

During the second summer, three outside evaluators were invited to the campus to talk individually and then collectively with faculty, and later to send written comments. Their remarks confirmed that, in the absence of faculty support for creation of a new department-like entity, courses with altered content looked no different to students, and students probably had little awareness of FPID. While few faculty members saw this as a major drawback, the evaluators were concerned. FPID, they suggested, was suffering from a visibility problem which was affecting its long-term viability.

The 1982-83 academic year was a watershed for both the College and FPID. A new president took office; faculty were beginning a complete curriculum overhaul; FPID focused on consolidating its progress on campus and extending its efforts at outreach.

By the end of this year, although they did not all see where FPID was going or what their own roles in the program might be, most faculty members had become aware of the program and its themes. A substantial number were teaching revised courses — most of which they had received support to rework, but some of which were totally new. (Some 20 courses had been affected by this time; Human Nutrition, Global Dynamics, and Agricultural Policy Issues had been offered, with students from the Issues course going out to give presentations to high school classes as part of their assignment.)

A conference on the sustainability of American agriculture, held in October 1982, attracted between 150 and 200 students, faculty, community people, and the media. The morning sessions were broadcast live over local radio, and three television stations aired coverage. (Two individuals also began a dialogue with Wilmington about bequeathing farms!) This event served two purposes — it gave FPID a tangible activity, unambiguously its own, which students and faculty could identify and support, and it created similar awareness, interest, and approval in a considerable area of southwestern Ohio.

A second conference in February 1983 on agricultural concerns in the Middle East attracted a good number of repeat attenders, as well as new. Articles in the student newspaper, a library display, items on campus bulletin boards, contacts with student organizations, and more campus programs — science seminars, convocations, and visits by speakers to classes — began to establish awareness of the program among students and credibility among faculty. Quarterly faculty meetings to share plans on FPID-linked courses were held, and a quarterly "update" describing program courses, activities, resource acquisitions, etc. was published. A list of FPID-linked courses was published and distributed campuswide to make the program visible.

By summer 1983, with course revisions well developed, a further change in the program blueprint was proposed. A need was seen for increased experiential understanding/involvement for faculty. During a third summer "workshop," 10 faculty had a compressed, two-week version of the "farm practicum" course (prior to its being offered to students that fall). (The format benefited from contact with the summer program at Luther College — see Chapter 4.) Farms, processing plants, grain elevators, chemical dealers, ag lenders, research labs, and many other locales with their noise and smells and color, made the intellectual abstractions come alive and gave personification to issues.

In December 1983, a group of about two dozen faculty members and community people (including the town mayor) spent a week in south central Mexico, visiting and comparing agricultural development projects of varying scope and intent. After talking and learning about the connection between agriculture and development, participants were given first-hand exposure to the circumstances in which the development process operates.

In July 1984, a smaller but similarly mixed group traveled to Nicaragua to see agriculture in a different context — physical, social, and political. About half of that group spent several days in Costa Rica. This Central American trip followed a third conference, "Agriculture and Revolution in Central America," at which the group discussed such issues as land reform, agricultural export policies, corporate exploitation, and effects of military policy on campesinos.

These first-hand experiences led to a number of programs which were presented to local civic organizations (Rotary, Kiwanis, etc.), classes, and faculty. They also resulted, with a minimal financial investment by the program, in much greater commitment by faculty to FPID and its goals.

During the last eight months of the grant, a school outreach program came into being, the realization of ideas formulated early in the life of FPID. By teaching Global French to fourth through sixth grades during their lunch break (with a phenomenal 40 percent voluntary participation — over 200 children), a part-time staffperson made contacts and investigated the kinds of materials teachers would use for food-related topics. Materials were sought and ordered — often at little or no cost, including many educational video programs (Wilmington classrooms are wired for video). The materials have been catalogued and computerized for easy access by teachers, and the College Education Department has taken on responsibility for their use and dissemination in the local school system, as well as their use in training future teachers. It is suspected that the focus on young people may have greater, long-range effects than the original emphasis on adult education and awareness — a goal that has been difficult to achieve.

As the grant period concluded, Wilmington added seven new courses important to agricultural literacy among students: Human Nutrition; practicum (U.S. Agriculture: How It Works); Agricultural Policy Issues; Third World Agriculture (a Sociology course making extensive use of films); Agricultural Genetics; Biocultural Geography (focusing on the origins of human selection/cultivation of edible plant materials); Food, Land Power, and People (a literature course comparing 19th Century and contemporary science fiction views of agriculture). At least a dozen revised courses, many of them basic, entry-level courses in various disciplines, were being taught. Coordination of the program was being subsumed under the Peace Studies program. Plans to set up a "Woolman Institute" center for experiential living and an "academic farm" (linked, respectively, to Peace Studies and Agriculture, with Biology participating in both) had moved along to the new purchase and/or dedication of land stage — each entity a tangible focus for continued multidisciplinary development of agricultural "literacy" and the pursuit of FPID program goals.

Lessons Learned

In retrospect, FPID was not simply about increasing agricultural literacy. It involved Wilmington College in reexamining its own self-definition, raising questions which could not be answered overnight. Given the tensions which existed between agriculture and the liberal arts at Wilmington prior to the grant (tensions not unlike those to be found at the larger, land-grant institutions), the selection of an outside, rather than an "inside," program coordinator, allowed the program to overcome many of the difficulties. Establishment of the preconditions under which the program could gain campuswide support was time-consuming. The lack of familiarity with agriculture and with the Wilmington community on the part of the program coordinator, both of which appeared initially to be drawbacks, may have, in fact, been worth the trade-off in time.

A second lesson concerns perspective. Written 18 months sooner, this retrospective would have been much less positive. Some plans which looked hopeless — school outreach, for example — suddenly fell into place in an unexpectedly strong way. When it was suggested near the end of the grant that a new course might have to be dropped, administrators asked that it not be and expressed their desire to continue to move toward making agricultural understanding a more central part of a general College curriculum.

The program could have improved its evaluation process. Some kind of original, baseline evaluation of student knowledge/awareness would have provided a useful comparison for ascertaining just how much the students were getting. Having outside evaluators come in more than once was useful for assessing change among faculty and administrators and suggesting improvements that could be made, but student body sizes made this impractical for that group.

As for community outreach, it is clear that one never starts with a blank slate. The need for program administrators to decide who they wish to reach and how they want to accomplish that objective, and then to touch base with all College people who have dealings with the "outside world" — alumni, admissions, development, etc. — is vital. It also is time consuming. But, judging from FPID results (for example, not nearly enough use was made of the statewide farm organization networks), perhaps no more time was spent than on the process (in terms of results). Still, as studies of community networking indicate (for example, those run by the Kettering Foundation on global education), it is almost impossible to build a lasting community base on a new structure, particularly as it deviates from the "bottom line," however community members individually and collectively define what that is.

The question of whether a program concentrates on education or on advocacy can come up, even when particular issues are not seemingly controversial. One would expect such a question to arise in terms of "organic" farming or animal rights, but it can come up even with soil conservation, etc. The program needs to be able to teach students more than what they can learn from the media. If it cannot, then philosophical questions surface among faculty, and even in the community.

How important is institutionalization of a program in agricultural literacy to overall institutional goals? In retrospect, this was a vital question which Wilmington only began to address as the grant ended, rather than prior to making its proposal. Often, grant proposals are, and must be written, by individuals. With no assurance that they will ever be funded, it makes little sense for institutions to invest substantial amounts of faculty time in proposals. At the same time, many grants involve substantial commitments of time and energy to goals that go beyond individual interests and individual interpretations about what will be good for an institution.

"The experience of focused intellectual collaboration" cited by an outside evaluator, was and will continue to be a vital part of FPID's success and continuing legacy at Wilmington College. The faculty development process which Kellogg Foundation funds made possible has forged new links between agriculture, biology, and sociology faculty in particular, and faculty from almost all departments generally. These relationships, as well as new projects evolving to give students applied learning opportunities, are the closest one can come to guarantees that FPID is at Wilmington to stay.

Chapter 8

World Food Issues Program
ADRIAN COLLEGE
Adrian, Michigan

Harvey Warrick

The Setting

Adrian College is a private college affiliated with the United Methodist Church. Its student body, numbering approximately 1,100 men and women, is drawn heavily from surrounding areas of Michigan and the upper Midwest. It is located in one of the top 10 most agriculturally productive counties in the state, yet it also has some geological features which make it easy to demonstrate extreme differences in soil productivity and enterprise suitability. It is this trait which made the College a suitable site for pioneering an agriculture-in-the-liberal arts program.

Program Plan

With the support of a grant from the W. K. Kellogg Foundation, Adrian developed an interdisciplinary World Food Issues course. Originally designed as a two-semester program, it aimed to cover aspects of food production and processing during the first semester, and to explore distribution and consumption issues in the second semester, including agricultural trade policies and ethical issues. Thus, the course was meant to be global in perspective and holistic in its approach.

The framework for the World Food Issues course was taken from a model developed by Dr. George Borgstrom, professor emeritus of Michigan State University. His "Hexagon of Survival" graphically illustrates the complex interrelationships of world

Harvey Warrick, past director of the World Food Supply program at Adrian College, Adrian, MI, is presently sales representative for Selective Feeder Company, Onsted, MI.

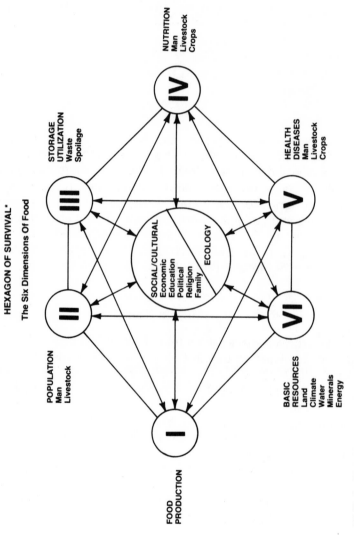

Figure 1

HEXAGON OF SURVIVAL*

The Six Dimensions Of Food

FOOD PRODUCTION

I

POPULATION
Man
Livestock

II

STORAGE UTILIZATION
Waste
Spoilage

III

SOCIAL/CULTURAL
Economic
Education
Political
Religion
Family

ECOLOGY

NUTRITION
Man
Livestock
Crops

IV

HEALTH DISEASES
Man
Livestock
Crops

V

BASIC RESOURCES
Land
Climate
Water
Minerals
Energy

VI

* Modification of the model developed by Dr. George Borgstrom, Michigan State University.

116

food supply (see figure 1). Establishing the linkage between agriculture and other areas of the chart provided the basic structure of the course.

The Foundation grant provided for a period of planning and training. Dr. Glen Dildine, professor emeritus from Colorado State University, facilitated planning sessions by helping the course instructors to develop a team concept, master effective teaching techniques, and construct methods of student evaluation and measurement. The papers he prepared for the planning sessions discussed such topics as: "Self-Concept Principles for Significant Learning and Teaching," "Some Thoughts on Possible Student Evaluation Procedures," and "Group Process — Productive Group Behavior and Development." Dr. Dildine also conducted half-hour interviews with each student at the conclusion of the course to gather information which would be helpful to the planning team when revising the course.

Out of this planning process came a course syllabus which listed the following goals and objectives: "The general goal of the World Food Issues course is to promote a deeper awareness and understanding of political, economic, social, cultural and ethical issues related to world food supply, and to develop attitudes and skills essential for responsible action."

The syllabus also specified several content and skill objectives. They included:

Content objectives

identify the major relationships between world food supply and nutrition, resource limits, population growth, food production, processing, distribution, and waste;

identify and compare production and consumption of food in various nations;

gain an awareness of the complexity of world food issues, and of the difficulty and necessity of dealing with them.

Skill objectives

develop observation skills through audiovisual, simulation, and field trip experiences;

develop skills in analyzing and synthesizing information;

develop skills in researching a topic;

develop skills in oral and written communication;

develop skills in setting goals for self-directed study along with a system of accountability;

develop sensitivity to group process and develop the ability to work with a group in a democratic manner.

Program Organization

Upon receipt of the grant, a project director was appointed by the president and academic dean. It was his responsibility to develop a World Food Issues course that would expand students' understanding of the world in which they live and that would prepare them to be useful members of the global community. The director was given the task of arranging for outside speakers and of planning field trips. In addition, he wrote the annual project reports and recruited faculty members for the teaching team.

Several criteria were used in selecting faculty members to teach the course. Individuals needed to have an interest in food issues. Additionally, they had to be willing to team teach. For example, faculty members from the Religion and Philosophy Department might be asked to teach segments on the ethical issues of food distribution and use.

Faculty members were informally invited to participate in the program. Individuals' participation in the effort hinged on whether or not they could fit the World Food Issues course into their teaching load for that semester. Members of the teaching team moved in and out of the course depending on the demands of their departments.

The World Food Issues course was team taught by five staff members each semester during the first five semesters; four persons were involved during the next two semesters; and three were involved until the end of the grant. The course is now taught by one faculty member. These interdisciplinary teaching teams attend all class sessions, in contrast to a multidisciplinary model which would find one or two instructors in class at the same time. Over the five-year period of the grant, nine different faculty members from seven disciplines were involved in the course. Their backgrounds included home economics, history, political science, sociology, biology, economics, and philosophy/ religion. The program director, an agricultural economist, also was a member of the teaching team.

Process and Product

Adrian College's World Food Issues course was comprised of units. The units included segments on the hungry in the United States and local feeding programs. U.S. agriculture production was introduced by looking at local agriculture production. One unit involved a tour of local farms and food-related businesses. Population and ethical issues also were topics of discussion in the units, as were nutrition and energy concerns. (See Appendix V for a complete list and description of the units.)

The course was designed to not only impart knowledge of agriculture, but also to motivate students to take action and to equip them with models or techniques to effect change. To accomplish this objective, the course combined subject matter with group process experiences. For instance, the class was divided into groups of five to eight students and each group was assigned a country to study. Using the "Hexagon for Survival" individuals in the group explored the six dimensions of food and then made a class presentation on their findings. They were encouraged to be imaginative. One group used the television series "Mission Impossible" format for their presentation and videotaped their introduction. This effort required teamwork in gathering props, arranging video time, researching the topic, preparing the script, coordinating the production of the videotape, and participating in the production.

Individual projects also were used to introduce students to agriculturally-related issues and concerns. For example, every student enrolled in the hunger and feeding units was asked to keep a record of his or her food intake for a three-day period. Comparisons of that record were made with recommended daily requirements for an average adult. This was done to show students where weaknesses in their dietary habits existed.

"Hands-on" experiences with agriculture were a critical component of the course too. Providing such experience was relatively easy since Adrian College is centered in a fertile agricultural area. Help with visits to farms was received from the Cooperative Extension Service, a local farm organization, commodity groups, and registered livestock breeders. Through such trips, students were able to follow a commodity from the raw product to the food counter — milk, for example.

A highly successful experience for Adrian College students was an overnight stay on a dairy farm. Students' images of what they expected and what they experienced were radically different. Class after class generally viewed farmers as "hicks" engaged in an occupation requiring more brawn than brain. After seeing the use of computerized bookkeeping systems, the employment of advanced technology in breeding livestock, and the enlistment of complete families in operating farms, they changed their attitudes toward farmers and farming.

Another successful field trip was an excursion to Chicago to visit the Institute of Cultural Affairs, located in a west side ghetto known as Fifth City. The Institute identifies factors blocking progress for inner city residents, and extends its findings to remote villages throughout the world. Methods developed at Fifth City have been replicated and refined in over 40 countries. Adrian College's purpose for exposing students to its experiences was to broaden their understanding of global development and to put them in touch with an organization that emphasizes participatory decision making.

Lessons Learned

The Adrian College experience has led to several conclusions which may be helpful to other colleges or universities interested in establishing agricultural literacy programs. The first, no doubt, is that faculty members originating from different disciplines and modes of instruction, no matter how interested in the subject matter, cannot be expected to function as a team without training and preparation. Adrian College's approach showed it to be an instrumental method in helping faculty members develop an effective working relationship with one another.

Second, a comprehensive strategy is needed to involve a greater number of faculty members in the program. This problem was not given enough attention by the project director. Ideally, faculty release time with compensation should be built into the program. Additionally, a series of workshops might bring together all faculty members interested in agriculture in the liberal arts.

Third, the College learned that experimentation with team teaching in a new field requires faculty members willing to take risks. It also calls for members who do not feel needlessly uncomfortable teaching in a class where others may have as much knowledge on a given topic as do they.

Fourth, "friendly" exchanges or disagreements between faculty members in class tend to make some students uncomfortable. One student commented: "It's like going to a friend's house and listening to his parents argue." Faculty members need to speak with a more unified voice or should clearly explain that disagreements are representative of the disparity of views on the issues, hence the importance of greater understanding.

Fifth, evaluation revealed that group projects need to involve a minimum of five and a maximum of eight students to be effective. Most larger groups tend to let a few people do most of the work. Shirking can be minimized by building a means of accountability into the group process system. For example, the College might ask students to rank themselves and all other members of a group for their contribution to the group project.

Finally, effective field trips require planning and careful preparation. Students must be thoroughly briefed about the purposes of trips and coached about what to look for at the sites. Detailed reviews after trips reinforce student experiences and place even greater emphasis on the relation of trips to class objectives.

It should be pointed out that the success of field trips and student experiences does not depend upon an institution having access to fertile, productive agricultural enterprises. While it is true that such sites serve as good demonstrations, they do not necessarily provide the most representative illustration of world food issues. Perhaps some of the following examples and suggestions will make this point clearer.

To introduce individuals to world food issues, students can keep a record of their food intake for three days. Comparisons of that record with recommended daily requirements for the average adult can be a very revealing experience. (Generally, much more attention is given to the diets of livestock on the farm than to the diets of our children.) As a learning experience, students might visit their campus dining hall to observe student food preferences and attitudes toward waste. Learning opportunities also exist when students bag groceries at a local market or work as aides to people filling out applications for food stamps.

Even in large urban areas there is likely to be someone with a garden which provides a large percentage of vegetables for their family. Industries concerned with drying, canning, or freezing food are probably close enough to visit. Experimentation in food production is occurring in the botany departments on many campuses. A trip to any of these sites can be an enlightening experience.

Clearly, world food issues is a fascinating and exciting topic on which to base courses, or parts of courses, in the liberal arts. A person need not be an expert on agriculture to be an effective advocate for agriculture in the liberal arts. Getting involved broadens and deepens awareness of some of the most pressing issues of our day. As Benjamin Franklin's grandfather is reported to have said: "It is better to strike a blow with a crooked stick than to spend the rest of your life searching for a straight one."

Chapter 9

The Humanities and Agriculture Program

THE UNIVERSITY OF FLORIDA
Gainesville, Florida

Richard P. Haynes

The Problem

The United States has developed one of the most highly productive and technologically advanced agricultural systems in the history of the world, yet few people seem to understand the social and environmental impacts of it. Institutions of higher learning are notably weak in providing the training and sophistication to facilitate this type of understanding. Agricultural professionals are increasingly specialized and from nonfarm backgrounds. Rarely do agricultural training curriculums provide an overview or opportunities to reflect on assumed values. Nor is this overview provided by the disciplines outside the agricultural curriculum. Historians, by and large, have failed to provide the basis for an integrated view and critical analysis of our directions in agriculture. Additionally, standard texts and courses in history do not give students an adequate appreciation of the role and the social costs of our current agricultural systems. Philosophers too have neglected all but a few basic questions about agricultural practices.

Agricultural ethics is an undeveloped field. The failure to raise agricultural issues in liberal arts courses, to examine value assumptions, and to discuss critically current agricultural policy has produced a major gap in the liberal education of citizens and future leaders. One source of this failure is a lack of intellectual interaction between agricultural and liberal arts educators, scholars, and researchers. It exists even among professionals within colleges, and is a major reason for the failure of professionals to develop the breadth of view required for intelligent and informed policymaking.

Richard P. Haynes is associate professor of philosophy and director of the Humanities & Agriculture program at the University of Florida, Gainesville.

There is need, then, to improve general knowledge and to stimulate debate concerning social issues that derive from current agricultural practices and policies. This need exists for political leaders, professionals, the general public, and especially for students who will be making social decisions in the next decades. Efforts to create an improved intellectual climate within institutions of higher education must be directed, therefore, at achieving greater intellectual interaction among liberal arts and agriculture professionals at the local level and across disciplines at the national level. Without the type of cross-fertilization brought about by transdisciplinary dialogue and educational, scholarly, and research oriented projects, it will be difficult to raise the level of sophistication about agricultural policy issues among professionals or students.

The Setting

The University of Florida is a multicollege land-grant University with more than 33,000 students. Its 18 professional schools and colleges include a College of Liberal Arts and Sciences (CLAS), which includes 32 departments and a number of interdisciplinary undergraduate programs. CLAS also staffs basic education courses for the other colleges and professional schools at the lower division level. The Institute of Food and Agricultural Sciences (IFAS) includes the Experiment Station research program, the Cooperative Extension Service, the College of Resident Instruction, and encompasses a School of Forest Resources and Conservation and a College of Veterinary Medicine. The University of Florida Graduate School administers 72 doctorate and 200 masters degree programs. Twenty-four of the doctorate programs are in the College of Liberal Arts and Sciences, and 18 are in agricultural fields that include about 90 different areas of specialization.

The budgetary process of the University of Florida tends to promote division between IFAS and the rest of the University. IFAS is a single budgetary unit, as is the J. Hillis Miller Health Center. Both are independent of the Education and General (E & G) budget, whereas CLAS is a part of the E & G budgetary unit of the overall University of Florida system.

IFAS provides for its staff and faculty many of the services that the University provides for staff in other colleges. The relative independence, together with a somewhat insular attitude toward colleagues in other budgetary units, has helped to perpetuate the traditional division of professional disciplines into agricultural and nonagricultural specialties; the separation of entemology from biology and agricultural economics from economics are examples. This insularity, even though it has historical roots in the rise of the agricultural professions, seems to be reinforced by what can only be described as an urban-based disdain by professionals in the liberal arts and sciences for agriculture as a profession and an activity. This attitude is often accompanied by the belief that there is little intellectual merit in the agricultural sciences. Reinforcing the prejudice against agriculture is the historical prestige that so-called "basic" or "pure" sciences have held in contrast to "applied sciences." Agricultural professions are isolated still further by career demands to specialize and publish, by the awkwardness of disciplinary jargon, and by the difficulties of promoting intra-campus intellectual interaction where little has existed in the past.

The humanities at the University of Florida have been significantly less well supported than at Florida State University at Tallahassee, as though there exists some unwritten agreement that humanities monies will flow to Tallahassee rather than to Gainesville. To combat this trend, CLAS has tried to improve its humanities programs by attempting to create closer ties with professional schools, especially by way of preprofessional programs.

In 1976, the University of Florida received a $900,000 grant from the National Endowment for the Humanities to develop a program of Humanities Perspectives in the Professions aimed primarily at prelaw, premedicine, pre-engineering, and prebusiness students. Courses were developed to demonstrate the value of humanities training as preparation for the specialized education of professional schools. Preparation of this type helps promote the learning of professional skills and provides a broader and more value-conscious context for professional specialization. Many of these courses have been absorbed into the CLAS curriculum, clarifying a role for the humanities in preprofessional education at this institution.

One of the lessons learned from this experience was that new courses, many of them team-taught by professional school and humanities faculty, are not always the most effective way of bridging gaps between academic disciplines. Team-teaching proved to be expensive and difficult to support on a continuing basis. It does not always provide a good experience for students or faculty, especially when faculty members use the classroom as a theatre for transdisciplinary communication without first having practiced cooperative behavior outside the classroom. A professional development program designed to counteract the narrow specialization encouraged by professional training and career advancement must precede or accompany multidisciplinary curriculum, if the latter is to succeed.

Although IFAS had not been involved in the original National Endowment for the Humanities project, several faculty members who had taught in the project thought about extending the concept to agriculture. Interactive processes between CLAS and IFAS had been developing slowly. Largely through efforts of some anthropologists, a weekly brown-bag lunch for social, food, and agricultural scientists was arranged to discuss topics of mutual interest. Out of this discussion group, several collaborative projects evolved. A small farming systems research project and a small farming systems seminar, for example, were developed as shared responsibilities of IFAS and anthropology faculties. A contract with Malawi in Africa to assist in the development of an agricultural college was also staffed with IFAS and anthropology faculties. Then, too, the Latin American Studies program and the African Studies program started to offer seminars on themes concerned with rural and agricultural development.

The spillover to the classroom, however, seemed to be confined largely to a few small seminars for upper division and graduate students. Courses which met the general education requirements of 900 agricultural majors and 18,000 CLAS majors rarely dealt with the social and political determinants of agricultural policy choices. These basic distributional requirements include nine hours of social sciences and nine hours of humanities. University of Florida program planners believed that by modifying some of these courses, agricultural issues could become more available to students. In addition, modification of the courses could serve pre-agricultural majors by providing them with a broader view of their field of specialization. In short, opportunities existed in this setting for extending some aspects of the original National Endowment for the Humanities program to agriculture. Given the general social significance of agricultural issues, the emphasis clearly would not be restricted to showing preprofessional students in agriculture how the humanities and social sciences can broaden professional perspectives. It would indicate how this broadened perspective contributes to and is an essential part of a truly liberal education for all students.

Program Plan

The Humanities and Agriculture program project was designed by two faculty members from the Philosophy Department, with cooperation and encouragement from other faculty and from the administration of CLAS and IFAS. When the project designers first thought about extending the "Humanities Perspectives in the Professions" concept to agriculture, they wanted to avoid team-taught courses. They knew that creating an interest in multidisciplinary projects was a long-range alternative to team-teaching and a means of modifying courses informally. When they tried to identify areas for course modification they naturally turned to the general education courses from which all students must select a certain number of lower division credits. They also knew that target populations were not simply agricultural or pre-agricultural students, but lower-division students in all fields.

Their first experiment involved a section of a philosophy course called Contemporary Moral Issues. A number of independent sections of this course are taught in the Philosophy Department each semester. Normally each instructor chooses a text which covers several current ethical issues, such as abortion, capital punishment, environmental issues, and preferential hiring. Different topics may be covered and different texts may be used for each section.

Two pilot sections of this course were designed. One covered several issues, including agricultural concerns. The other concentrated *entirely* on ethical issues in agriculture. Following the department's practice, descriptions of these courses were posted prior to registration; as is usually the case, almost none of the 35 students enrolled in each section read the course descriptions beforehand. Their choice of sections was blind; rather, their main motivation for choosing the course was that it satisfied three of the nine-hour humanities general education requirement, that Contemporary Moral Issues sounded interesting, or that it fit into their schedule. To be sure, the eight sections normally offered each semester are always over subscribed.

Both pilot sections were well received by the students though individuals enrolled in the section entirely devoted to agricultural issues expressed disappointment the first day of class when the topic of the course was announced. They remained in the class, however, when the moral issues in agriculture were described. One of the main lessons learned from this experience was that students find the subject matter of agriculture very interesting once they get past their widespread bias against it. This suggests that "agriculture" in the title or description of a course detracts from its enrollment appeal.

Guest speakers from IFAS also were brought into the classroom to provide students with an opportunity to inquire about technical issues, and, in some cases, to hear the other side of some issues. Many of these speakers had much to offer the class. When pilot sections were offered again the following semester, speakers were found to be less willing to participate. It was later suggested by several sources that some guest speakers had found the "confrontive" atmosphere of the class "threatening." These same sources generalized that "agriculture faculty are not used to this type of confrontation." Course leaders were not sure whether they had learned another lesson, since they had no independent means of verifying the accuracy of the sources, who the faculty were, or what counted as "confrontive."

By now the University planners had worked out a set of goals for a curriculum development program in agricultural literacy for a land-grant college, and a rough plan for reaching them. The program goals were to: introduce agricultural issues in some liberal arts courses that satisfied general education requirements in the social sciences and the humanities; initiate a professional development program aimed at broadening the perspectives of both liberal arts and agricultural professions, so that course modifications would become professionally institutionalized; and gradually create a climate of interest among *all* students in topics which relate the humanities and social sciences to agriculture. As the last goal is achieved, more advanced courses could be offered in the liberal arts curriculum with "agriculture" as part of the course title, e.g., A History of Agriculture in the United States, and some humanities courses, could be introducted to the agricultural curriculum.

The first step was to identify a number of courses that could be modified, and faculty who would be willing to participate in making the initial changes. Two basic U.S. history courses, a basic anthropology course, and the philosophy course previously mentioned were chosen. Each course met an education requirement. Several medium-level, well-subscribed history courses and one political science course also were identified as appropriate vehicles for agricultural literacy materials. Instructors of all courses were sympathetic with the project. Finally, several more advanced courses were flagged for eventual development, including courses in literature, philosophy, history, and anthropology.

With this plan in mind, extramural funding was sought to help stimulate project development and go beyond the initial pilot offerings. Six basic areas of support were identified:

summer salaries for faculty to develop or modify courses that would become part of the agricultural literacy program;

salary compensation to departments for the first year that the courses were offered;

salary for a part-time faculty director and a minimum support staff of one half-time secretary and one half-time graduate assistant;

travel budget for faculty enrichment to attend conferences and begin building a network of concept supporters;

funds for consultants and speakers to enrich the campus program, contribute to professional development, and assist in developing a network of interested scholars; and

funds for evaluating the effectiveness of new or modified courses and for disseminating information about the program to other institutions.

This extramural support would provide incentives for faculty and departments, and it would provide the means for attracting campuswide, as well as nationwide, attention.

To give the project identity and to follow through on the theme of "Humanities Perspectives in the Professions" that already was well known, the University of Florida decided to call it "The Humanities and Agriculture Program." The word "humanities" in the title was not meant to exclude other liberal arts fields from being vehicles for agricultural literacy or contributors to an understanding of agricultural policy. The title emphasized the human dimensions of agriculture.

At this point (Spring, 1980), the campus planning group learned that the W. K. Kellogg Foundation had provided start-up support for agricultural literacy programs at a number of liberal arts colleges. An agricultural literacy program at a land-grant college, of course, would have somewhat different goals. With a substantial agricultural faculty offering courses in most of the major fields of agriculture, there certainly was no need to bring agriculture onto campus. The problem, rather, was getting non-agricultural students to use this expertise, as well as getting agricultural experts and their students interested in broader questions than they were used to handling.

Since problems faced at the University of Florida in this regard were similar to those at other multicollege campuses with colleges of agriculture, the University approached the Kellogg Foundation with a proposal to: develop an agricultural literacy program at the University of Florida; assist in developing a national network of educators and scholars committed to the goal of agricultural literacy; promote agricultural awareness at other land-grant colleges; and develop a model curriculum in agricultural literacy for land-grant colleges.

A timetable for carrying out these plans was then drawn up and commitments from the administration of the involved colleges were secured to match start-up support from the Foundation and to take over full support of the program when its initial three-year development phase was completed. Commitments also were secured from the faculty of each involved college to support the program's teaching, planning, and professional development activities.

This timetable called for 50 percent of the outside support to be spent the first year. Thus, contributions of the Foundation and University were to be divided 80/20 the first year, 50/50 the second year, and 20/80 the third year. This division was followed except that, as the importance of encouraging development of a sympathetic scholarly community became more apparent during the first year, additional extramural funding was secured to help support a national conference in the second year.

The first summer was used by faculty members to develop course modifications or, in some cases, to devise entirely new courses. Modules then were introduced during the fall and spring semesters. Monthly faculty development colloquia also were held, with faculty of the fields involved in the program taking turns in making introductory presentations. Each colloquium was concerned with how agricultural literacy fit into the field under review.

A revised timetable called for a workshop in the spring to identify major issues that an agricultural literacy program should address and the parts of an agricultural literacy curriculum which needed additional scholarship and text-material development. This workshop was followed in the fall by a major national conference, designed to promote dialogue among liberal arts and agriculture professionals and to stimulate curriculum-supporting scholarship. As expected, the conference drew national attention to the idea of agricultural literacy and helped develop a network of concept supporters.

A final dissemination conference was conceived for the third year, designed to share results with other institutions that might be interested in developing similar programs. It was felt that the exchange of information and generation of new ideas expected at this conference would provide a good basis for a monograph to serve as the final dissemination vehicle of the model being developed.

Program planners also felt that the first year of the program would provide enough teaching experience with agricultural literacy modules to enable them to begin thinking about training faculty for other institutions. So the timetable provided for one internship in the second year and two in the third year. Internships were to be continued as long as needed. Teaching workshops and short courses also were planned for the fourth year.

Program Organization

At the beginning of the project, the project innovators had some fairly definite ideas about how to organize the program. As they gained experience, however, and after the project administration was supplemented by an IFAS program coordinator, some ideas were modified. These ideas and their modifications are worth reviewing since the method of organizing a new program determines its eventual outcome.

Initially, the project was to be administered in the CLAS. It would have a faculty director who would devote 50 percent of his time to administration of the program. A planning committee, consisting of faculty from involved CLAS departments and from several departments in IFAS, would be actively involved in planning various phases of the program, especially professional development. Professional development would continue to be a major part of the program, along with the curriculum development. It was decided not to grant degrees or certificates in the program.

The program needed to be located in the College of Liberal Arts and Sciences, at least initially, because the target student population was composed primarily of undergraduate students taking CLAS courses. Yet, program planners were concerned that housing an agricultural literacy program outside of the College of Agriculture would be perceived as an intrusion on its turf. For a while feelings of territoriality did threaten to interfere with the type of cooperation between colleges necessary to make the project work. But the planners continued to believe that basing the program outside the college of agriculture was the correct decision. To the extent that this type of program succeeds in breaking down college and disciplinary barriers to multidisciplinary research and teaching, the issue of which college should administer the programs becomes less significant.

The program clearly needed a dedicated director devoting at least half-time to championing the project and its goals. Since the director's commitment to the project would likely not lead to immediate career advancement, it was important to choose the project director from among the senior faculty with tenure, and support him/her in special administrative ways. As the project matured, it became obvious that the director would have to take an increasingly active lead in developing momentum for the overall program.

Towards the end of the first year of the program, the directors of all agriculture-in-the-liberal arts programs being supported by the Foundation met at a small networking conference. It was there the program planners began to understand that building and sustaining a dynamic program would require imaginative solutions to overcome the inertia of a career-oriented university structure. The series of colloquia that had been held on a monthly basis were not providing the momentum needed. Initial colloquia were well attended, as was a series of meetings with a consultant from Pomona College whose "pep talks" generated enthusiasm among the faculty involved. After the first six months, though, attendance at colloquia started to wane. Interest was restored and new program advocates were identified only after holding an ambitious workshop toward the end of the first year and organizing a national conference midway through the second year. These experiences showed that successful professional development required focused projects and attracted transdisciplinary interest. Identifying, organizing, funding, and directing these projects became almost the full-time job of the director.

Strong support for the program and its staff from both of the involved colleges was also quickly seen as a necessity. The University had, from the start, attempted to involve faculty from the two colleges in the planning of teaching and program-focusing projects. Repeatedly the college deans gave indications to their faculty of their interest in and support for the program. Without this strong support, building faculty involvement would have been impossible. The deans also provided additional financial support for program projects, staff and equipment, and office space. At the end of the second year IFAS agreed to provide a program coordinator on a one-quarter time basis. The IFAS program coordinator provided strong support and significantly facilitated cooperation between the colleges.

Achieving broad faculty involvement in project planning proved to be more difficult. The program started out with a six-member planning or advisory committee. Its function was to plan the professional development phase of the project. The committee initially met monthly and then it met more frequently to plan the workshop and the national conference. As interest in the program grew, especially after the first workshop, the committee was expanded. Meetings were organized to keep members in a problem-solving mode rather than as ratifiers of actions taken by the director. Two committee members withdrew because the meetings were being held too frequently and required too much time. Ironically, when major projects were first announced, some people protested that turf-intrusion decisions were being made without full consultation with all interested parties. The program planners' response to this protest was to open arms to more input.

By the middle of the second year, it became increasingly clear that planning committee members were not sufficiently involved in key projects to provide sustained and serious input. Consequently, meetings became primarily informational, and occurred less frequently. Replacing them, to some extent, were efforts by the director and the IFAS coordinator in planning projects, and more direct involvement of interested faculty in professional development projects that had clear-cut tasks and goals. Part of the reason for this change in administrative structure was success in clarifying program goals and project tasks.

A monthly local newsletter also was instituted at the beginning of the third year to keep interested faculty and administrators apprised of program projects. This newsletter, which is mailed to about 200 people, replaces Planning Committee minutes previously circulated to about 75 interested parties. In addition a printed brochure now is available which explains the purpose of the program and some of its achievements. It includes a description of current semester course offerings, and is mailed to all faculty advisors on a regular basis.

An important discovery of the program was the need to develop "program-focusing" projects. Full awareness of the need for such projects emerged in discussions among the directors of programs given start-up support by the Kellogg Foundation. Among their common concerns was the challenge of keeping programs going when outside funding and the dramatic advantages it gives run out. As already noted there was waning interest in monthly colloquia toward the end of the first year of the program. Though there were many supporters of the idea that students needed to know more about agriculture, no one seemed to be interested in discussing how these modifications were to take place. Likewise, many people were interested in discussing substantive agricultural issues, but few wanted to explore how these issues could be incorporated into course modules.

The planners decided to use the consultant money provided for by the grant to conduct a forum for a national discussion of these issues. The first year workshop and the second year conference generated a stronger general commitment to the program. Now people were talking about developing projects that addressed specific issues. The notion of "project" came to play a more important role.

Thus, the idea emerged that a dynamic and viable program was possible only if there were multidisciplinary projects to keep focusing attention on program themes. This is especially true in a university setting where, despite official lip-service to teaching and curriculum development, careers are advanced by research and scholarship. The realization led to a kind of "spill-over" or "trickle-down" theory of curriculum development. If academics start developing an interest in topics for scholarly reasons, these topics will find a way into the curriculum. Hence, a continuous search for funding to finance multidisciplinary research and scholarship came into being.

Process and Product

Evaluating the impact of a program is the best way to test the clarity with which participants conceive project objectives. The Humanities and Agriculture Program of the University of Florida chose the following as its primary program goals:

increase the general sophistication of undergraduate students about social and environmental factors that affect and are affected by various modes of agricultural production and distribution;

increase students' interest in and care about these factors, especially as they influence the making of agricultural and food policy;

broaden the perspectives of academic professionals working in agriculture, the social sciences, and the humanities, especially where these fields ought to relate more closely;

stimulate academic professionals to engage in transdisciplinary projects of professional education, research, and scholarship, especially when investigation is an important preliminary to informed debate about the full range of alternative agricultural and agricultural-related policies; and

stimulate interest in the development of similar programs at other institutions of higher learning throughout the country, and facilitate development of such programs by helping to organize network-building and staff-educating projects.

During the first year of the program's development, evaluation centered solely on the program's success in achieving the first goal and then only insofar as the newly modified curriculum produced these effects in the contexts of individual classes.

To determine the effectiveness of newly modified courses during the program's first year, students in each course were asked to write brief essays on the same topics at the beginning and end of the course. Subjects were chosen to permit measurement of students' awareness of social and environmental issues that are pertinent to the evaluation of alternative agricultural and agriculture-related policies. An evaluative consultant was hired to develop an instrument for measuing issues-awareness levels and alternatives-assessment abilities. The consultant trained a panel to evaluate the students' essays, using this instrument. The instrument and its use were independently assessed by a professional evaluator for the College of Education at the University of Florida. The Statistical Analysis System program "T-test" was used to compare pre- and post-measures on 160 randomly selected papers. A statistically significant gain in each area was found.

Regarding the second goal — interest in and caring about

agricultural policy issues — there is considerable evidence that, once exposed to these issues, more than half of the students do come to care about them. This fact was illustrated when students enrolled in Contemporary Moral Issues in Agriculture, unaware of the course title, reacted negatively to announced topics. But a single discussion of the issues caused students to stay in the course and to respond favorably to the topics. Many students have followed up their interest in these topics by taking other related courses, including African Studies and Latin American Studies courses that are concerned with agricultural issues. The ultimate test of success in changing students' interests, of course, is their subscription to courses with "agriculture" in the title. In the final phase of the three-year start-up program, interest-level instruments were designed and applied to determine if this happened.

Regarding goals three and four, there is evidence of some success locally and nationally. Even when financial incentives are no longer available to encourage development of agricultural literacy modules, faculty members who were party to original modifications are continuing to strengthen their course offerings and to increase their number.

More sections of Introduction to American History and Contemporary Moral Issues in Agriculture are being offered than originally proposed. New courses are being suggested by faculty who wish to participate in the program. There is growing interest among agricultural faculty to modify courses in order to attract non-majors. Total program offerings have increased from 20 sections the first year to 29 the third year, and enrollments have increased from 1,275 students the first year to 3,600 projected for the third year.

Several professional development projects undertaken in the program had wide-ranging impacts. Professionals from various fields have undertaken research and writing on topics that relate agriculture, social science, and the humanities. The national, multidisciplinary conference "Agriculture, Change, and Human Values," held in October of 1982, was attended by approximately 300 researchers, educators, and policymakers, including over 100 from off campus. Participants represented a variety of views from various fields. This effort was a major step in promoting the concept of multidisciplinary dialogue, research and scholarship in interface areas. It raised consciousness among professionals about the significance of agricultural issues in the liberal arts curriculum and about ethical and value issues in the agriculture curriculum. Conference participants from almost 20 disciplines included 81 faculty members, 9 college deans or vice-presidents, 6 government officials, and 17 representatives of private groups.

Supplementary funding support for consultants was obtained from the University of Florida Division of Sponsored Research, the W. K. Kellogg Foundation, and the Rockefeller Foundation. Postconference evaluation forms indicated that 70 percent of those attending felt the conference did a good-to-excellent job of meeting learning expectations, while 26 percent rated it merely adequate. Postconference inquiries from nonattenders about the availability of conference papers has been high.

Since the conference, a number of institutions have expressed interest in starting similar programs.

Lessons Learned

The development of this program has been a lesson for all in interprofessional dynamics. The University participants feel reluctant to generalize from the experiences, however, since it is not clear to what extent the perceptions of success and failures reflect unique local situations, narrowly conceived alternatives, unperceived results, or poorly formulated goals. Comparing notes with institutions that have tried something similar has proven to be a valuable experience. Network-building workshops and conferences also are essential ways to learn lessons and see beyond immediate concerns. Hence the networking conference for directors of the 11 agriculture-in-the-liberal arts programs supported by the W. K. Kellogg Foundation held in Claremont, California, in the spring of 1982 was exciting, informative, and encouraging. It was from this conference that the University planners began to sense the program's potential, the similarities of problems that crossed institutions, and the possible uniqueness of the sets of problems they might encounter in developing a program at a large, multicollege campus. Since the University of Florida planners have not had the opportunity to compare notes with program developers at other large institutions, the lessons concentrated on here may or may not be applicable to other large multicollege campuses with colleges of agriculture.

Two major problems worth discussing are how to attract students to new courses, and how to staff new courses. Both problems may have dimensions that are unique to larger campuses. Following are some suggested solutions to them.

Student Enrollment

Attracting students to new courses is a greater problem on large campuses than on smaller ones because there is more competition for the attention of students. So much advertising takes place on a large campus at any given time that is hard to get across any particular message. When the difficulty in getting attention is coupled with biases against "agriculture," new courses with "agriculture" in the title are precarious ventures. This can be avoided by the following means.

Introduce agriculture to liberal arts courses that are already well-subscribed.

New courses, especially with "agriculture" in the title, would be better introduced after programs already have made progress educating students about agriculture in courses taken for other reasons, and educating faculty advisors about the value of new courses. Informal faculty education occurs in professional development activities or projects. Former advisor education is probably more difficult. Workshops for advisors might be effective, but attracting attendance is a problem. This is an area where incentives might be helpful, though the University of Florida has not tackled the problem.

Acquire and use data on the value of agricultural literacy in the job market. This is an area about which the University currently lacks information. It is initiating some surveys to help provide answers here.

Staffing Courses

Where formula funding is used in public universities, staffing new courses is difficult until consistent student demand develops. Campus size, complexity, and emphasis on research also intensify the difficulty of promoting the kinds of faculty interactions needed to build program support. Curriculum development and teaching, in spite of public disclaimers, normally are not seen by faculty or administrators as important elements of career advancement.

Since faculty in a research-oriented university generally prefer to teach in areas where they also write and accumulate publication records, one solution to staffing problems is to create a broader base of professional interest and commitment in fields needing research and scholarship. Research and scholarship are, in fact, greatly needed in fields which relate agriculture to the social sciences and humanities. To stimulate and support research and scholarship in these areas, several sources of fundings are rapidly becoming available. These sources include foundations that traditionally support science-technology studies and humanities-science and professions-bridging projects.

Professional development projects in the agriculture-in-the-liberal arts fields tied to curriculum development projects should also be able to find funding from organizations exploring increased continuing education roles for the liberal arts, or broadened liberal education roles for traditional extension service. Organizations interested in promoting roles for the humanities and liberalizing arts should be sympathetic to this type of curriculum development project. In the field of agricultural education, curriculum development projects oriented toward ethical and social issues will likely be viewed more sympathetically in the next five years.

Extramural Funding

The University of Florida's program planners asked for extramural funding from the Kellogg Foundation after developing a fairly clear conception of what was to be accomplished and how. The support of a number of faculty members and the administration of the two involved colleges also was secured. The concept was tried out for two semesters in a pilot course. More than 50 percent of the grant was committed to be used during the first year of the project. A fairly significant amount of these funds was used to provide summer release time for selected faculty members to develop new courses and modify existing ones. A large amount was used to buy a portion of the faculty's time from departments to teach new courses or new modules. In retrospect, the University planners feel that other programs should not use their funding in this way.

Existing programs have already developed an ample repertoire of agricultural literacy courses and modules for liberal arts courses that faculty from institutions wishing to develop their own programs could draw upon. Course materials from these efforts and training by personnel involved in older programs can be made available. Sending faculty to short courses and workshops would be a more economical use of funding than simply purchasing release time for a summer or a semester.

Nor should departments be compensated for offering modified

courses when modifications do not affect class enrollments. It does not cost departments anything to do so when courses are already well-subscribed. If departments wish to experiment with new courses, purchased release time might be justified in a few instances but they should remain a comparatively small drain on extramural funds, especially at this stage of the development of the agricultural literacy concept. Nor should extramural funds be used to purchase extra time for team-teaching projects. Team teaching is expensive and should be undertaken, if at all, as part of a professional development experience for involved faculty members.

The more economical uses of extramural funds are professional development projects such as networking workshops and short courses, faculty incentives in the form of travel, subsidies and visiting speakers, and program administration. The University of Florida's program planners also feel that extramural funding would be used more effectively if it were spread more evenly over a three- or four-year period. Publicity received on campus when grants are announced give a boost to projects. However, ongoing publicity serves to draw new faculty into programs in greater numbers toward the end of the first and the beginning of the second year. This did not happen at the University of Florida because, by that time, most of its start-up funds were committed. The attracting power of start-up funding should be preserved over a longer time-frame to take advantage of emerging interests.

Identifying New Program Sites

It is important, in the next several years, to encourage development of additional pilot agricultural literacy programs. In selecting institutions to serve as a core of examples, it is recommended that foundations use two criteria: 1) evidence of strong administrative commitment and strong leadership from respected senior faculty — in multicollege universities, from both the agriculture and the liberal arts colleges; and 2) evidence of a strong willingness to work cooperatively with and support networks of programs.

It is generally advisable to select institutions where there are several faculty members in liberal arts fields who already have professional interests in agricultural topics. Within each of the cooperating colleges of a particular program, there needs to be a faculty "product champion" who will carry the new program through several years of its development. This individual should be supported by an administrative "protector" who will shield the product champion from the risk engendered in making large commitments of time to innovative work, especially in the area of curriculum development.

New programs should provide strong support for this program manager/innovator, including release time to develop the program. New programs should also have adequate resources for professional development programs and innovative curriculum developments, which may oppose existing reward structures. Programs will have the greatest chance of success in institutions which are willing to take seriously the problem of changing reward structures to favor despecialization projects and curricula. This includes adopting new criteria for publications in the area of transdisciplinary projects, program development, and professional development.

The Role of Workshops and Short Courses

Short courses and workshops probably accomplish more to stimulate interest and learning than almost any other technique. They can be very efficient uses of resources for curriculum development. They provide focus for intense interchanges of ideas and frequently epitomize the academic community. Conferences and workshops, especially when they involve a commitment of time off from routine work, are genuinely exciting and renewing. Consequently, if incentives can be provided for attendance, they will have great spinoff benefits. Not only can they function as support for existing programs and encouragement to develop new ones, but they can be used to achieve desired curricular changes independent of beginning a structured program.

If the desired long-term goal of agricultural literacy must begin with consciousness raising in higher education, it may turn out in the long run that program development is only an intermediate step towards the institutionalization of other vehicles for consciousness raising. The ultimate end is greater integration of agriculture into the general educational curriculum. So the goal may not be to develop permanent programs in all major institutions, but to incorporate knowledge about agriculture into its rightful place within the whole educational curriculum.

Chapter 10

Conclusions: Context and Continuity

Gordon K. Douglass

The underlying thesis of this book is that our traditional ways of teaching and learning about the liberal arts are inadequate, and that they would be significantly improved by augmenting the vital *content* of the liberal arts with insights about agriculture and by paying more attention to the *context* within which it is received, assimilated, and used.

Improving the content of the liberal arts with insertions of agricultural concerns would enhance teaching and learning for the reasons outlined in Chapter I: Agricultural issues are compellingly important in a world of increasing imbalance between human population and the resource base that sustains it; they are ideally suited to help bring new coherence to the primary objectives of a liberal arts curriculum; their study can help to focus the attention of many disciplines on a common object of investigation, an especially useful result in a time of intense academic specialization; and their serious exploration has enormous potential for advancing an institution's understanding of the linkage between thinking about an issue and experiencing the issue first hand.

Context

The experiential essays contained in this book speak mostly about the curriculum of agricultural awareness programs as if their authors regard the transmission of this vital *content* as the primary, if not sole, objective. But first impressions can be deceiving. Each essay also makes the point that the *process* of transmission can make an enormous difference in the quality of learning that takes place and in the potential for what is learned to change people in positive ways. In discussions of liberal education, this linkage of *what* is learned to *how* it is acquired is too often neglected.

In all the main traditions of formal education, the dominant understanding of teaching and learning is that instructors teach and students learn, with very little attention given to the processes involved. The "funnel" mode of instruction, which provides a channel through which instructors pour information and students fill their memories, is disgracefully prominent on the campuses of American colleges and universities. It is true, of course, that good teachers have always been sensitive to the conditions of effective learning and have adapted their art accordingly. But it is also true that educational systems favor standardized curriculums, lock-step calendars, and unremittent classroom venues that stiffle instructional innovations by even the most gifted teachers.

If the essays in this volume are correct, then a major flaw in the design of formal education is the relative absence of the mixture of observation and practical work experience that complements and reinforces students' academic studies.

All authors of this book point out that verbal descriptions of agriculture do not communicate the challenges facing students that experiential education — the coupling of classroom learning to personal experience — does. In the classroom situation, issues are generally defined by academic discipline. But in the field, on the farm, or around the centers of decision making, disciplines cannot be distinguished. When discussing the loss of prime agricultural land, the viability of small farms, or the limits of our natural resources, all relevant sources of insights such as economics, government policies, social structures, and ecology, must be considered together. Experiential education that is harnessed to important academic studies is holistic education, and this kind of learning forces students to seek better ways of putting information to work in their lives.

The authors of the preceding chapters also contend that the context of agricultural education has a profound effect on the rate of learning and the amount of knowledge retained. Students learn concepts, theories, and descriptions of agricultural systems more quickly with hands-on experience, and they learn to question conventional wisdoms more readily than in the normal campus instructional environment. Though few, if any, carefully structured studies of retention rates have been carried out by the experimental colleges, students' written responses to field experiences and the subjective judgments of program leaders uniformly affirm the importance of experiential learning to the task of improving student abilities to process, file, and retrieve agricultural insights long after they first were introduced. Since truly informed decisions can be made only with a rich mixture of savvy and knowledgeability, experiential agricultural education serves students and their society well in later life.

Organization

Because programs at the experimental colleges differ significantly, it would be surprising to find program leaders drawing the same conclusions about their respective experiences from organizing agriculture in the liberal arts programs. They do not. Yet similarities do show up unexpectedly, and it may be useful to summarize these.

First, they all agree that broad faculty involvement is critical to successful programming. A generous cross section of disciplines should be represented on the program oversight group, including representatives from anthropology, biology, economics, ethics, history, political science, and sociology. This breadth of representation helps to ensure a friendly reception of the program; it also permits agriculture to be viewed holistically, released from the narrowness usually accorded the field. A system of incentives also must be set in place to make certain that broad participation occurs. This means that a considerable amount of flexibility should be built into program budgets in order to assure breadth and vitality for the program.

Second, practical experience has taught the experimental colleges that intellectual and administrative leadership of programs must be strong and continuous. Such leadership may come from within the existing faculty or it may be recruited from outside the institution. If the former model is chosen, care must be taken to select faculty leaders who will command the respect of their peers and who will be willing to serve at least two or preferably three years; otherwise, momentum and a sense of common purpose easily can be lost. Recruiting an outsider to give leadership to the program helps to assure continuity, but runs the risk of failing to provide the strong faculty linkages essential to program success. In the latter case, administrative oversight should remain in the hands of regular faculty members.

Third, several of the colleges have found that program publicity, when wisely designed and targeted, is an effective instrument for building constituent support both within and outside the college. In the beginning, the audience will be mostly internal. But as programs mature and a broader audience begins to take note, media stories, interpretive brochures, and program newsletters can be used effectively to cultivate independent sources of support for programs, as well as to encourage similar ventures in other institutions.

Finally, some schools have discovered useful ways to harness student enthusiasm for agricultural programs to the task of organizing effectively. Student involvement in the selection, preparation, and implementation of public events is a good way to guarantee an audience and an easy way to care for guests. Giving students considerable discretion in the organization of some activities, such as editing a program newsletter or staging a film festival, also has been used as an effective means of delegating responsibility for certain program tasks. Two schools even have student steering committees to advise and assist the program director and the faculty oversight committee.

Continuity

It is somewhat early to tell whether the obvious vitality of programs will be preserved after the Kellogg Foundation's initial grants have been used up. The question remains: Is there real life after Kellogg?

Currently there is little concrete evidence that agriculture-in-the-liberal arts programs will find a permanent place in the curriculums of liberal arts colleges after the newness fades. In two cases, the "core" courses which were created to anchor programs have been continued, and the library materials acquired during the grant period have remained accessible and useful in succeeding semesters. New library acquisitions have dropped off at these institutions, on the other hand, and the intensive public events programs on agricultural topics which enlivened campus discussions have mostly disappeared. At a third institution, the number of courses or course modules designed to implement agricultural program objectives has been cut in half since funding support expired, and there is a fear that further cuts will be made as faculty turns over and interests change. Student-sponsored activities, however, seem to have retained their vitality. Thus, the most solid evidence to date suggests that programs of agriculture in the liberal arts are by no means assured indefinite life.

The *expectation* of most faculty members and many students now participating in such programs, though, is that they will continue. Part of this optimism is based on fuzzy notions about what it costs to hire new faculty or to put on major public events, or about how easy it would be to raise the money to finance such outlays. Major undertakings are expensive and money is relatively hard to find these days. But a significant part of such optimism may be entirely rational: Some agriculture-in-the-liberal arts activities do not take a lot of money.

Once courses in the regular curriculum have been altered to include important agricultural information; once new courses have been developed and folded into the regular course offerings of institutions; and once food and agricultural questions have been affirmed as legitimate college-sponsored public events, they can be assured a place in the college as long as their sponsors care. Undoubtedly, tradeoffs will continue to exist as long as resources are limited and faculty preferences are diverse, but maintenance costs need not be as high as start-up costs, especially if the initiating programs helped develop a strong sense of shared enterprise among faculty program participants.

Developing a new concentration, on the other hand, will cost a lot of money, and it is clear from the experiences of the experimental colleges that outlays of this sort will require the infusions of substantial amounts of new money not previously targeted by college administrations.

Whether other colleges will choose to initiate agriculture-in-the-liberal arts programs remains to be seen. Those that do — and the hope is that there will be many — stand to make enormous gains in bringing agriculture into the college and the community. As one program participant so aptly put it: "It isn't enough for students to just have scientific knowledge and abilities. They must learn to apply that knowledge to real life situations like feeding the world adequately for the indefinite future."

APPENDICES

Appendix I

Pomona College
Conference and Symposia
Speakers and Topics

Mini conference on the "Size of Farms and the Quality of Life in Rural America"
Walter Goldschmidt, professor of anthropology, University of California, Los Angeles; B. Delworth Gardner, professor of agricultural economics at the Berkeley and Davis campuses of the University of California, and director of the Gianninni Foundation; and E. Phillip LeVeen, economist, Public Interest Economics West, San Francisco.

"Mechanization, the University, and the Farm Workers"
Ralph Abascal, chief counsel, California Rural Legal Assistance, Sacramento.

"Social Impact of Agricultural Mechanization and the Changing Agricultural Research Priorities"
William H. Friedland, professor of sociology, University of California, Santa Cruz.

"Can a Botanist Wear Blinders? Externalities, Agriculture Policy and Crop Production"
James P. Bennett, assistant professor of vegetable crops, University of California, Davis.

"Alternatives in California Agriculture"
Martin Barnes, editor, *Winds of Change;* leader in Rural Action program, Winters, California; farmer, Capay Valley, California.

"Farm Labor and the Structure of California Agriculture"
William Myers, coordinator for the Small Farms Viability Planning project, Office of Rural Affairs in the Department of Employment, State of California, Sacramento.

"Soils, Contemporary Agriculture, and Future Productivity"
Parker Pratt, professor of soil science, University of California, Riverside.

"International Agricultural Development: Perspectives from a Third World Biological Ecologist"
Ranil Senanayake, National Heritage Trust and the Neosynthesies Research Centre, Sri Lanka.

"Issues of Agricultural Planning in the Third World"
Leonard Joy, professor of international agricultural development, University of California, Davis.

"Chinese Agricultural Development Policy"
Eugene Anderson, professor of anthropology, University of California, Riverside.

"The Peace Corps and Agriculture Development in West Africa"
Jeff Hill, agricultural development specialist, University of California, Davis.

"Seminar on First and Third World Relations and Food"
Lord Caradon, former United Kingdom ambassador to the United Nations.

"Socioeconomic Development, Oil and Agriculture in Mexico"
Jorge Calderon, economics faculty, National Autonomous University of Mexico.

"Rural Development in China"
Ben Stavis, visiting professor of political science, University of British Columbia.

"Roles for International Research in Increasing Food Production"
Alex McCalla, professor of agricultural economics, former dean of College of Agricultural and Environmental Sciences, University of California, Davis.

"Appropriate Technology in Ethiopia"
Soloman Teklu, agricultural development specialist, University of California, Davis.

"The Problems of U.S. Food Policy in Central America"
Blase Bonpane, professor of political science, California State University, Northridge.

"Private and Public Sectors and the Small Farmer in Mexico"
Theodore Downing, associate professor of anthropology, University of Arizona.

"U.S. Agriculture: Its Beneficiaries and Benefactors"
Paul Barkley, Rainier National Bank, professor of agricultural economics, Washington State University.

"An Alternative Path of Development: Agricultural Sustainability Through Buddhist Wisdom as a Way of Life," and *"Buddhist Thought in Action: Agrarian Reform and the National Heritage Trust"*
C. Upali Senanayake, Sri Lankan Buddhist leader and agrarian reformer, founder of the National Heritage Trust of Sri Lanka.

Panel discussion of Mr. Senanayake's presentations
John B. Cobb, Ingraham professor of theology, School of Theology; James W. Gould, professor of history and International Relations, Scripps College; C. Dean Freudenberger, professor of international development studies and missions, School of Theology at Claremont; Bruce Long, professor of world religions, Claremont Graduate School, director, the Blaisdell Institute; Jerry A. Moles, director, Food, Land and Power program, Pomona College.

"An Ethical Alternative to the Exploitation of Natural Resources"
Michael Soule, conservation biologist and geneticist, executive vice president, Institute for Transcultural Studies.

"World Population and the Earth's Carrying Capacity"
Anne Ehrlich, senior research associate, Department of Biological Sciences, Stanford University.

"African Food Deficits and Alternative Paths for Change"
Steve Commins, coordinator, Food and Agriculture project, African Studies Center, UCLA.

"Nature and Madness — The Psychohistory of Human Ecology"
Paul Shepard, Avery professor of human ecology, Pitzer College.

"Agricultural Policies and Problems in the Philippines"
Joel Rocamora, professor of political science, University of California, Berkeley.

"California Agricultural Problems Through French Eyes"
Francois Terrasson, assistant director, Nature Conservation Service, Paris; Charles Touzan, senior researcher, National Institute of Agricultural Research, Toulouse.

"Agricultural Revolution and Social Change: An Historian's Perspective"
Gordon E. Mingay, professor of agrarian history, University of Kent.

Appendix II

Principal Papers from
"Agriculture Sustainability in a Changing World Order" Conference at Pomona College

"A Global Strategy for Agriculture"
Orville Freeman, chairman of the board, Business International Corporation; secretary of agriculture in Kennedy and Johnson Administrations.

"Theology, Ethics, and Sustainability of Agriculture"
John B. Cobb, Avery professor of theology, School of Theology at Claremont and Claremont Graduate School, California.

"Changes in the Availability of Agricultural Land, the Quality of Soil and the Sustainability of Agriculture"
William E. Larson, professor and head, Department of Soil Science, University of Minnesota.

"Energy and the Sustainability of the American Agricultural System"
William Lockeretz, research associate, School of Nutrition, Tufts University.

"A Call for a Revolution in Agriculture"
Wes Jackson, director, The Land Institute, Salina, Kansas.

"The Ecological, Energetic, and Agronomic Systems of Ancient and Modern Sri Lanka"
Ranil Senanayake, ecologist, National Heritage Trust, Colombo, Sri Lanka.

"Hope, Ideas, and Our Only Alternative — Ourselves and Our Values: National Heritage and the Future of Sri Lanka Agriculture"
Jerry A. Moles, associate professor of anthropology and director, Food, Land and Power program, Pomona College.

"Socioeconomics, Equity and Environmental Quality in North American Agriculture: Alternative Trajectories and Future Developments"
Fred Buttel, associate professor of rural sociology, Cornell University.

"Economic Perspectives on U.S. Agriculture: Policy Issues and Options"
Kenneth Farrell, director, Food and Agricultural Policy program, Resources for the Future, Washington, D.C.

"Land, Water, and Energy Resources in Agriculture"
Roger Revelle, professor of science and public policy, University of California, San Diego.

"Resource Management in Tropical Agroecosystems in Southeast Mexico"
Stephen Gliessman, assistant professor, Environmental Studies, University of California, Santa Cruz.

"The Requirements of Sustainable Agroecosystems"
Miguel A. Altieri, assistant professor, Division of Biological Control, College of Natural Resources, University of California.

"How the World Feeds Itself"
Vernon W. Ruttan, professor, Department of Agricultural and Applied Economics, University of Minnesota.

"Stewardship and Agriculture: Sustaining Productivity"
Honorable George E. Brown, Jr., member of Congress, overseas agricultural research programs and policies in the House of Representatives.

Appendix III

The Consortium on Agriculture and World Hunger Summer Seminar

Basic Readings

Sandra S. Batie and Robert G. Healy, "The Future of American Agriculture," *Scientific American* 248:2 (February 1983).

Harold F. Breimyer, "The Decline of the Family Farm," from *Food Policy and Farm Programs,* ed. Donald F. Hadwiger and Ross B. Talbot. *Proceedings of the Academy of Political Science* 34:3 (1982).

Lester R. Brown, "World Population Growth, Soil Erosion, and Food Security," *Science* 214 (27 November 1981).

Willard W. Cochrane, *The Development of American Agriculture: An Historical Analysis.* Minneapolis: University of Minnesota Press, 1979. Chs. 7, 8, 11, 14, 19.

Nick Eberstadt, "The Legacy of Theodore Schultz, *RF Illustrated* (October 1980).

Donald F. Hadwiger, "Nutrition, Food Safety, and Farm Policy," from *Food Policy and Farm Programs,* ed. Hadwiger and Talbot.

R. J. Hildreth, "The Agricultural Research Establishment in Transition," from *Food Policy and Farm Programs,* ed. Hadwiger and Talbot.

Uma Lele, "Rural Africa: Modernization, Equity, and Long-Term Development," *Science* 211 (6 February 1981).

William Lockeretz, Georgia Shearer, and Daniel H. Kohl, "Organic Farming in the Corn Belt," *Science* 211 (6 February 1981).

Alex F. McCalla, "Politics of the Agricultural Research Establishment," from *The New Politics of Food,* ed. Donald F. Hadwiger and William P. Browne. Lexington, Mass.: Lexington Books, D.C. Heath & Co., 1979.

Julius K. Hyerere, "The Plea of the Poor," speech at Howard University, Washington, D.C. (5 August 1977).

John B. Peterson, "Agronomists and the Food Chain," *McGraw-Hill Yearbook of Science and Technology* (1981).

Society 17:6 (September/October 1980). Nine articles collectively titled "Food Crisis?" under the general editorship of Vernon W. Ruttan.

John A. Schnittker and Martin E. Abel, "Food Aid and Food Trade."
D. Gale Johnson, "Catastrophe or Illusion?"
Nick Eberstadt, "Malthusians, Marxists, and Missionaries."
Alain de Janvry, "Agriculture in Crisis and Crisis in Agriculture."
Richard Critchfield, "Javanese Villages: The View from Below."
David Seckler, "Food as Fuel."

Luther P. Gerlach, "The Flea and the Elephant: Infant Formula Controversy."
C. H. Shah, "High-Cost Calories: Food Preference and Poverty."
Vernon W. Ruttan, "How the World Feeds Itself."

A Time to Choose: Summary Report on the Structure of Agriculture. Foreword by Bob Bergland. United States Department of Agriculture (January 1981).

Luther Tweeten, "The Economics of Small Farms," *Science* 219 (4 March 1983).

United Nations Association of the U.S.A, Iowa Division: Committee Report and Recommendations, "Feeding the World . . .FAO and the United States."

M. Mitchell Waldrop, "Deep changes taking root in U.S. agriculture," *Chemical and Engineering News* 59 (1 June 1981).

Appendix IV

The Consortium on Agriculture and World Hunger
Summer Seminar

Consultants and Topics

1981

William L. Brown, chief executive officer and chairman (retired), Pioneer Hi-Bred International, Inc.: International interdependence.

Eber Eldridge, professor of economics and extension economist (retired), Iowa State University: Land use.

Joseph R. Hanson, deputy administrator for program operations, Farmers Home Administration (retired): Marketing.

Robbin S. Johnson, assistant vice president of public affairs, Cargill Incorporated: The United States and the world grain economy.

Arnold Paulsen, professor of economics, Iowa State University: Government policy.

Vernon W. Ruttan, professor of agricultural and applied economics, University of Minnesota: Technological change.

Lauren K. Soth, food and agriculture columnist for the *Register and Tribune Syndicate:* The interlocking issues. Patterns of farm ownership.

Hylke Van de Wetering, professor of economics, Iowa State University: World hunger.

1982

Harold Breimyer, professor of agricultural economics, University of Missouri: Patterns of farm ownership.

Beverly Everett, vice-chair, U.S. National Commission for UNESCO: Rural Life in underdeveloped countries: a personal report.

Donald F. Hadwiger, professor of political science, Iowa State University: The politics of agricultural research.

Robbin S. Johnson, assistant vice president of public affairs, Cargill Incorporated: The United States and the world grain economy.

William E. Larson, professor and head, development of soil science, University of Minnesota: Changes in the availability of agricultural land, the quality of soil, and the sustainability of agriculture.

Wayne Moyer, associate professor of political science, Grinnell College: The politics of U.S. international food policy: structural factors affecting the grain embargo decision.

Chet Randolph, commodities brokers and farm analyst for Iowa Public Broadcasting: Selling right: market strategies for today's farmer.

G. Edward Schuh, professor and head, department of agriculture and applied economics, University of Minnesota: Policy issues involved in U.S. grain export practice.

Lauren K. Soth, food and agriculture columnist for the *Des Moines Register and Tribune Syndicate:* The land: are we using it up?

Hylke Van de Wetering, professor of economics, Iowa State University: On the use of general equilibrium modes in agricultural policy analysis.

1983

Donald N. Duvick, director, plant breeding division, Pioneer Hi-Bred International, Inc.: Genetic diversity as affected by plant breeding activities.

Wes Jackson, codirector, The Land Institute: Toward a unifying concept for sustainable agriculture.

Robbin S. Johnson, vice president of public affairs, Cargill Incorporated: The United States and the world grain economy.

William E. Larson, professor and head, department of soil science, University of Minnesota: Changes in the availability of agricultural land, the quality of soil, and the sustainability of agriculture.

Wayne Moyer, associate professor of political science, Grinnell College: The politics of U.S. international food policy.

J. W. Pendleton, professor of agronomy, University of Wisconsin-Madison: International agricultural research centers, and the example of transferring technology to the small rice farmer.

Charlotte E. Roderuck, director, The World Food Institute, Iowa State University: Nutrition and related problems in developing countries.

Lauren K. Soth, food and agriculture columnist for the *Des Moines Register and Tribune Syndicate:* Where do we go from here in food and agricultural policy?

Marty Strange, codirector, Center for Rural Affairs: The decline of agrarian agriculture.

Ramakrishna Vaitheswaran, professor of political science, Coe College: The political economy of world hunger: third- and fourth-world perspectives.

Participants

1981

Wilfred F. Bunge, professor of religion (Luther).
Duane Carr, associate professor of chemistry (Coe).
Paul A. Christiansen, associate professor of biology (Cornell).
William G. Flanagan, assistant professor of sociology (Coe).
Benjamin F. Graham, professor of biology (Grinnell).
Edward T. Hill, professor of mathematics (Cornell).
David L. Lyon, professor of biology (Cornell).
Mary Hull Mohr, professor of English (Luther).
Wayne Moyer, associate professor of political science (Grinnell).
Harland S. Nelson, professor of French (Grinnell).
Morris Parslow, professor of economics (Grinnell).
Robert F. Voertman, professor of economics (Grinnell).
Bruce Willis, associate professor of linguistics (Luther).

1982

Peter C. Bloch, assistant professor of economics (Grinnell).
Douglas Hanson, associate professor of art (Cornell).
David M. Hay, associate professor of religion (Coe).
Eugene Hinman, professor of geology (Cornell).
Earl J. Leland, professor of history (Luther).
Harland S. Nelson, professor of English (Luther).
T. Hardie Park, professor of economics and business (Cornell).
James Rhodes, professor of political science (Luther).
Floyd Rockwell Sandford, associate professor of biology (Coe).
Kathryn D. Schweer, associate professor of nursing education (Coe).
Judith B. Smith, assistant professor of education (Luther).
Elliott L. Uhlenhopp, associate professor of chemistry (Grinnell).
Ramakrishna Vaitheswaran, associate professor of economics (Coe).

1983

Steven Feller, assistant professor of physics (Coe).
Lowry C. Fredrickson, professor of psychology (Coe).
Vivian Y. Heywood, associate professor of art (Cornell).
Patricia Johnson, assistant professor of social work (Luther).
Alan R. Jones, professor of history (Grinnell).
Roger M. Knutson, professor of biology (Luther).
Michael J. Kovalchik, assistant professor of physical education (Coe).
Geneva Meers, professor of English (Cornell).
Harland S. Nelson, professor of English (Luther).
Diane C. Robertson, associate professor of biology (Grinnell).
Randolph A. Roth, assistant professor of history (Grinnell).
Michael L. Sandberg, associate professor of business administration (Coe).
Richard S. Ylvisaker, professor of philosophy (Luther).

Appendix V

Adrian College
World Food Issues Course Units*

1. The Hungry in the United States
   Hunger in America, a filmed CBS documentary; reel one followed by discussion of questions: "What were the circumstances?"

2. The Hungry in the United States
   reel two of *Hunger in America* followed by discussion of the commonalities and differences.

3. Local Feeding Programs
   Panel from local agencies and organizations involved in feeding programs, e.g., Meals on Wheels, food stamps, school lunch, Community Action Center, Salvation Army food kitchen, local food bank, Associated Charities, Ministerial Association, Expanded Nutrition, WIC program.

4. Local Feeding Programs
   Panel from local agencies; assign student to volunteer two hours at one of the agencies and report back to the class.

5. Local Agriculture Production
   A look at types of agriculture in the area, compared with the rest of the state or region; how do climate, soils, markets, urban sprawl, zoning, tax structures influence the crops grown?

6. Tour of Local Farms or Food Related Business
   Local food distribution center or processing plants (dairies, bakeries) are possibilities.

7. Panel of Farmers
   Organic vs. traditional farming, issues facing farmers, shifts or trends locally or regionally; where are locally grown commodities processed or marketed?

8. U.S. Agriculture
   Major Crops, climates, soils, water supplies; agribusiness; effects of government and legislation; trade agreements.

9. Energy Use in U.S Agriculture
   Energy intensive agriculture, based on reading E. R. Duncan, *Food Problems.*

10. Energy uses in the Food Chain
    Firewood the Other Energy Crisis, a film produced by Church World Service, Elkhart, Indiana; Energy-intensive U.S. model compared with labor intensive systems in china.

---

*The activities listed under each heading represent only a few of the possible activities that might be conducted each semester.

11. U.S. Agriculture Position in the World
What and where do we export? What do we import? History of food aid; a comparison of production in U.S. with that of China, USSR, the European Economic Community, and India.

12. Population
Maragoli, a filmed study of a Kenyan village available from University of California, Berkeley; reel one followed by discussion on cultural and economics dynamics.

13. Population
Reel two of *Maragoli;* many discussion possibilities; biosphere considerations.

14. Population
Reports by class members on current population developments: China, Third World nations, family planning program, legislation.

15. Ethical Issues
World population, based on reading in *Ethics for a Crowded World,* Center for Ethics and Social Policy, Theological Union, Berkeley, California.

16. Ethical Issues
Lifeboat ethics; Hardin vs. Freudenberger; U.S. aid to India vs. China without aid.

17. Introduction to Human Nutrition
History, minimum requirements, sources.

18. Human Nutrition
Film *Diet for a Small Planet:* Analysis of student diets for the past three days; a vegetarian meal or sample foods.

19. Nutrition
Comparison of diets in other cultures; food additives, infant formula, Eastern view of food as medicine; ailments related to diet.

20. Health and Disease
The effect of disease on food use, malnutrition and undernourishment among children; slides by a medical missionary; Peace Corp speaker.

21. Ethical Issues of World Income Distribution
Film *Beyond the Next Harvest,* Mass Media; "Only the poor go hungry."

22. Storage, Utilization and Waste
Measure waste in food service on campus, local school lunch programs, local restaurant; loss during harvest; storage losses in tropics; loss to rodents and insects; cheese distribution dilemma in the United States.

23. Appropriate Technology
Development strategies; row crop agriculture in tropics compared to native methods; labor intensive vs. fossil fuel based production methods; infra-structure; distribution patterns.

24. Reports by Students on Term Papers
Team using country theme; individual topic selected from the Hexagon.

25. Reports Continued, Introduction to Simulation or Development Model
Possible simulation topics:
development plan for a theoretical nation; water allocation hearing in Southwest; agricultural use vs. industry and recreation;
establishing an international grain reserve;
sell the family farm to developers or expand to include son and new city bride.

26. Simulation or Development Model
Possible development models: LENS, a method developed by the Institute of Cultural Affairs, Chicago, with village development projects in over 40 nations; create ministries and adopt a national development budget.

27. Simulation or Development Continued
The simulation ties the course together and illustrates the interrelationships of the subjects covered during the course.

28. Simulation Wrap-Up and Review.

*". . .for the application of knowledge
to the problems of people."*